*The mist gathered slowly, just a faint coolness and dampness around the stones. . . . Then Robert noticed the silence. . . . Fog now blanketed the ground within the circle of stones. Jennifer was just a gray shadow of herself, still digging down toward the hidden slab of rock.*

*The coldness of the fog soaked into Robert . . . he suddenly wanted to push the soil back into the hole that he dug . . . but the cold seemed to have reached his brain and he had no more power over his thoughts . . .*

IN THIS compelling time-slip novel, a girl and a boy from the twentieth century are carried through the Circle of Time into the year 2179. There they are caught up in the courageous struggle of a peace-loving people trying to protect their simple and humane way of life from the assaults of a barbaric mechanized society who would conquer and enslave them.

Through rich layers of time and meaning, Margaret Anderson has woven an intriguing tale of science fantasy in which the present becomes the past and the future is now.

IN THE
CIRCLE
OF TIME

# IN THE
# CIRCLE
# OF TIME

Margaret J.
Anderson

ALFRED A. KNOPF
New York

Library of Congress Cataloging
in Publication Data
Anderson, Margaret Jean, 1931–
    In the circle of time.
Summary: Two children are hurled into the
future as a result of their hunt for three
12-foot stones missing from an ancient
Scottish stone circle.
[1. Space and time—
Fiction. 2. Scotland— Fiction] I. Title.
PZ7.A54397Ik [Fic] 78-10156
ISBN 0-394-84029-1 ISBN 0-394-94029-6 lib. bdg.

For Frances Foster

IN THE
CIRCLE
OF TIME

# chapter 1

"It seems a foolish sort of idea," Mrs. Guthrie said in a worried voice. "You'll end up by being late for school and maybe even getting lost."

"I won't be late, and of course I won't get lost," Robert promised. He picked up his backpack and left the house hurriedly before his mother could say more.

Mrs. Guthrie followed him to the door and watched as he ran down the rough lane that led to the main road. Even after he had disappeared from sight behind the ragged hawthorn hedge she still stood there—a tall, spare woman with gray hair pulled back from her face in a tight bun.

"Getting up at this hour of the morning to draw a picture of those stones," she muttered to herself, shaking her head. "As if he couldn't have done a

3

picture of the cottage or the mountain for the old man."

But even as she said it she knew that a picture of the cottage or the mountain would not have satisfied the old man. It was the Stones of Arden that interested him, you might even say obsessed him.

The old man was her father, Dougal Ballentyne, and all his life he had lived in a tiny cottage on the other side of the mountain between the East Sands and the moor, just a few miles from the old stone circle called the Stones of Arden. The moor had provided him with a sparse living—peat for his fire and rough grazing for his sheep—but the sands had always been his enemy. The winds, blowing from the northeast, kept the sands on the move; gradually they had covered most of his land, and finally threatened his house.

The government officials had stepped in and had given him a new little council house over in Baldry, close to the shops and the pub and the church. You'd think he would be pleased to live in a new house that looked out on a little patch of garden instead of a waste of sand. But he wasn't grateful at all. He kept saying that he missed seeing the stones lit by the morning sun.

That was why Robert had said he would paint him a picture of the stones glowing in the sunrise. And *he* could do it. Robert's paintings were good.

Mrs. Guthrie gave a sigh and went back through to

the kitchen. She added some coal to the fire, pulled out the damper to heat the water, and then cleared the few dishes from the breakfast table. As she worked, she found herself still thinking about the stones. Who had put them there in the first place? Why did they have such a hold over people? She tried to remember her father's stories about them—just fairy tales, of course. And yet. . . . Once, when she had been very young, scarce old enough to walk, she had wandered out onto the moor and the fog had rolled in. When they found her hours later, she was wrapped in a strange, soft gray cloak that didn't belong to her. . . .

But there was work to be done with Mr. Guthrie away at the sheep sale. She hadn't even milked the cows! Mrs. Guthrie pushed all thoughts of the stone circle out of her mind and went purposefully out to see to the animals.

Robert had climbed the flank of Ben Arden, the great mountain that separated their glen from the North Sea. As he came down out of the cloud that shrouded the higher land in a damp mist, he stopped and gazed over the moor, stretching empty and re-mote, all the way to the sands and the sea beyond. Later in the summer the moor would blaze pink and purple with the heather bloom, but now it was a carpet of muted browns, soft greens, and black stretches of peat bog. Faint wisps of mist clung to the hollows, and Robert could see the stone circle, small and insignificant, dwarfed by the vastness of the moor. It was a long distance away. He would have to hurry.

He loped down through the bracken. Reaching level ground, he slowed his pace and chose his way more carefully. In places the ground was unsafe. Those solid-looking cushions of bright green sphagnum moss would yield under his weight, sucking him into the treacherous black bog. It was better to stay on the clumps of heather even though they scratched his legs.

From time to time he paused to look at small flowers—sundews, bog asphodel, and orchids—so strangely delicate amid the woody heather and coarse bracken. But he could not stop for long because the sun would not wait; besides, he had to get to school on time, although that was not uppermost in his mind.

He climbed a slight rise, his right leg dragging as it always did when he was tired. From there, in a saucer-shaped depression below him, he could see the stones—huge rectangular slabs, ten in all. From the spacing of the stones it appeared that there had once been thirteen of them, for there were three gaps—two gaps close together with one stone between them, and the third across the circle. The stones were of granite, the same rock that broke through the thin soil on the craggy side of Ben Arden and lay scattered as great boulders here and there across the moor. Though crude and rough, they nevertheless gave the appearance of having been selected carefully and placed in the circle for some unknown purpose by a forgotten people. It was as if the touch and memory of those distant people still clung to the stones, setting them apart from all the other granite rocks on the moor.

Robert walked slowly around the circle, then sat down on a rocky outcrop, the sun behind his shoulder, and took out his sketching pad. He had a box of watercolors, but he knew that there was no way he could capture the variety of colors in the rock. He had discovered that rocks weren't just gray or brown or black. They contained all the colors that had gone into the making of them, deep in the ground, long ago.

Robert scowled at the rocks and then at his drawing. His rocks didn't look solid enough, old enough. How do you make a rock look old, he wondered. Drawing used to be fun when he hadn't worried so much about how things turned out, but lately he could see everything in his mind so much more vividly than he could put it down on paper. If only someone could help him with his drawing—maybe give him lessons—but there was no hope of that. Not with the way his father felt about it. Drawing had been all right when Robert was little—it was something to do during the long period when he was sick—but now that he was eleven his father thought that he should spend all his time working on the farm. Only because his father was away at the sheep sale had he managed to talk his mother into letting him take his painting things here on the way to school. There wouldn't be many chances like this. He had to get the picture right.

With an exasperated sigh, Robert glanced up at the stones again. Immediately, his painting was forgotten. A tall, thin girl was standing beside one of the stones, her red-gold hair glowing in the sunshine. For a moment Robert thought that it was one of the Shape-shifters, or even the Bean-Nigh, from his grandfather's stories. Somehow she seemed to have risen right out of the ground. But the vision faded quickly when he realized that it was just Jennifer Crandall who was in the class above him at Locharden School.

She had apparently had some trouble in reaching the circle. Her pants and tennis shoes were stained black with mud—maybe that was why Robert had imagined that she had risen from the ground—and her face was mud-streaked where she had pushed back her hair with dirty hands. Although the morning was still cool, she was hot and sweaty and out of breath as if she had been running part of the way.

Jennifer had only recently come to Locharden, but everyone knew her. For one thing she was hardly inconspicuous with that red hair, and for another she was from America. Her father was working for the North Sea Oil Company. Her family hadn't been able to find a house in Aberdeen or Dundee, so they had rented the old Taylor Farm down the glen from the Guthries.

"What are you doing here?" asked Jennifer, the first to recover from the surprise of seeing someone in this deserted place. "At first I thought you were a sheep."

Robert felt his face grow red. He was never quick at thinking up things to say to people, especially girls.

"What's your name?" she asked.

"Robert Guthrie."

"I'm Jennifer Crandall."

"I know," said Robert.

"How do you know? Do you go to Locharden School?"

"We go on the same school bus. I sometimes get on at the foot of the glen near your place."

"How come I've never seen you?"

Robert gave a little shrug. He could have said that she hadn't noticed him because she was always too busy trying to make a big impression on Danny Lowrie. But then it could have been because Robert had this way of being invisible. When they chose teams for soccer nobody ever noticed him until he was left over at the end.

"What are you drawing?" asked Jennifer, crossing the circle to look at Robert's paper. He would rather not have shown her, but she picked up the sketch and held it out in front of her.

"Hey, that's O.K.! I wish I could draw like that."

Robert took back the drawing and silently stuffed it into his backpack.

"What are you doing here?" he asked.

"I meant to get here at sunrise," Jennifer answered. "But the sun rises terribly early here, doesn't it? The only way would be to stay here all night, but my mother probably wouldn't let me. She'd have a fit if she knew how early I got up today, but I made sure she didn't hear."

"Why did you want to be here at sunrise?"

"Don't you know what day this is?"

"Thursday," answered Robert after a moment's thought. "Yesterday was Wednesday, the day of the sheep sale."

"I mean the date," said Jennifer impatiently. "It's the twenty-first of June, Midsummer's Day."

"What's so special about that?" asked Robert, puzzled.

"Don't you know that crowds of people gather at Stonehenge on Midsummer's morning to watch the sun rise over the Heel Stone?"

"And you thought you would find the same sort of thing going on here?"

"No, of course not! But the arrangement of the stones could easily be connected with Midsummer's Day. The people who built these stone circles worshipped the sun and moon and often lined up the stones to mark the seasons or predict eclipses and things like that."

"How do you know that?" asked Robert.

"We visited Stonehenge when we first came over here and I got a book about it. I'm going to be an archaeologist."

"Well, this isn't Stonehenge."

"That's exactly why I have decided to make a study of it. People have been puzzling over Stonehenge and digging around there for centuries. It's been overworked. I'm going to decode the Stones of Arden!"

"But there's nothing to decode—just ten stones."

"Thirteen!" said Jennifer triumphantly. "Do you see those spaces there? Three more stones were in the circle originally, and that's important. One for each lunar month of the year. Probably their calendar began on the longest day. That's why I had to be here at sunrise—to make observations. You live around here. What do *you* know about the stones?"

"Well," began Robert slowly. "My grandfather would be the one to ask about that. He lives over in Baldry now, but he used to live in a cottage over there near the sea. He knows lots of stories about the olden times—how, once every hundred years, the stones walk from here out to the headland above the sea, and the awful things that happen to people if they see the stones move."

"That's just superstition," broke in Jennifer in a withering voice. "You always get superstitions built up around these old places. But that's not archaeology. What we need to do is to dig for artifacts from around here and have someone do carbon-14 dating on them."

Robert felt rebuffed. Besides he didn't know what Jennifer was talking about with her carbon-14 dating. "You won't find much digging in a bog," he said flatly.

"We could find the fallen stones for a start," said Jennifer, going over to one of the gaps and beginning to tear up handfuls of peaty soil.

"You won't find anything there," said Robert, watching her. "They've probably been hauled away years and years ago."

"Don't be silly! Why would anyone come this far and take three stones?" asked Jennifer. "It's far more likely that they fell and were gradually covered with dirt and overgrown with plants."

Robert scowled at her, but Jennifer continued to pull at the tough roots and was soon digging down into the dark, peaty soil. It annoyed him that she was so sure of herself.

"I don't think real archaeologists dig like that," said Robert. "We saw a movie about it at school once. They do it with teaspoons and clean everything off with a camel's-hair brush so that they don't miss or damage anything."

"It depends on what you're looking for," Jennifer pointed out. "We're trying to find twelve-foot slabs of rock. You wouldn't go after that with a teaspoon! Why don't you try digging in the next gap on the other side of that stone?"

Robert knelt down and began to pull up handfuls of heather and black soil and roots in a halfhearted way. It was a waste of time, but he wasn't going to get any more drawing done while Jennifer was around.

Crouching over his digging, Robert felt a sudden chill in the air as though a cloud had covered the sun. He shivered and looked up to see a thick fog swirling and boiling around the stones. Robert was used to the sudden sea fogs that came up on this part of the moor but he had never encountered a mist like this before. Usually it rolled in from the northeast in a solid bank, like a low cloud, but this mist seemed to seep out of the ground, out of the very stones. He turned to remark on the strangeness of it to Jennifer and, although she was just some eight feet away, he could see her only dimly, a strange, wraithlike figure crouched between two standing stones. She was still so absorbed in clawing out handfuls of dirt that she seemed unaware of the sudden change in the weather.

"Robert! I've found something!" Jennifer's voice floated through the fog.

At the same time Robert's knuckles scraped against hard stone. The fog was now so dense that Robert couldn't see Jennifer at all, and the coldness, the silence, and the isolation frightened him. On a sudden impulse he pushed some dirt back down over the patch of stone he had uncovered and packed it down hard.

The fog was lifting, swirling and blowing away; yet there seemed to be no wind. Only a waiting stillness in the air.

13

And then Robert could see Jennifer clearly, dark eyes staring at him from a white face. Her eyes had an unnatural, unfocused look, and when she spoke to him her voice was hoarse and strained.

"What happened?" she whispered. "Where have they gone? Who were they?"

Robert shook his head slowly. "I didn't see anyone —only the fog. There was no one else here."

"There was!" Jennifer insisted. "There were people digging over there—in the gap between those other stones. They were kneeling on the ground digging. They had made a huge hole. I saw them through the fog."

By now the last wisps of fog had dissipated and the sky was again blue. Robert stood up and walked slowly across the circle to the gap between the stones. He looked at the ground. It was completely undisturbed. Jennifer hung back, visibly shaken.

"No one's been digging here," said Robert. "You would be able to tell."

"But there was! You must have seen them, too! People with long black hair and strange clothes. They were digging in the soil with sticks and with their hands."

"Did they see you?" Robert asked.

"I don't think so," said Jennifer slowly. "They were too busy digging the hole. It was—well—it was like a grave."

With these words Jennifer burst into a storm of

tears. "I'm scared," she wailed. "I don't like this place."

Robert stood there, uncertain of what he should do or say. At least Jennifer's noisy crying dispelled some of the feeling of tension and unreality that had surrounded them. He picked up his backpack, slung it onto his shoulders, and said, "I think we should get away from here. If we don't get going we'll be late for school."

The commonplace words seemed to release them from some kind of enchantment. Being late for school was an ordinary sort of worry, one they could both cope with.

"What time is it anyway?" asked Jennifer.

"Quarter past seven," answered Robert. "But it will take us more than an hour to cross the moor and cut over the side of Ben Arden and get down to Baldry Road where the bus stops."

"I'll have to go home first and change," said Jennifer, looking down ruefully at her pants and shoes. "Besides, my mother will wonder what's happened if I don't show up for breakfast. I didn't even tell her I was going out."

"You won't have time to change and eat breakfast and still get the bus."

"Mom will take me in the car if I miss the bus. She's done that before. She'll take you, too, if you like. You might as well come in and have breakfast with us."

"I've got a jam sandwich in my pack," said Robert. "I'll eat it while I'm waiting for the bus."

"Do you often do this? Go somewhere before school?" Jennifer asked.

Robert shook his head. "This is the first time. My dad's away at a sheep sale so it was a good chance. Early morning is the only time the light is right for drawing the stones."

"Can't you come here when your dad's around?"

Robert picked his way carefully around a boggy bit of ground. "He thinks drawing is a waste of time. Anything that hasn't to do with farming is a waste of time in his opinion."

They entered a jungle of shoulder-high bracken that cloaked the mountainside, and for a long time they climbed in silence. Robert's foot was dragging and he was short of breath, but he didn't want to admit to Jennifer that he needed to rest so he forced himself to go on. When they were finally well out of the bracken and had reached the top of the hill, Jennifer threw herself down on the short turf. Robert sank down beside her.

"How did you know the stones were there?" he asked her, when he had got his breath back.

"One weekend when Dad was home we hiked over the moor to the coast and we came across the stones. We go hiking most weekends—I love your Scottish hills."

"You might feel different if you had to chase after

sheep on them in all kinds of weather," said Robert grimly. "Try walking these hills in February or March, looking for new lambs in a blizzard."

"Or in a fog, I suppose," said Jennifer, standing up and stretching.

"Just what did you see in that fog?" Robert asked, unable to hold back his questions any longer.

"Nothing," said Jennifer, looking at him calmly. "I've been thinking about it. I must have imagined it—what with the mist and all that. After all, *you* didn't see anything."

"Strange things do happen there. My grand-father—"

"You and your grandfather," Jennifer broke in angrily. "I'm interested in what's real—not a bunch of fairy tales."

"But you *did* see something," Robert persisted. "I could tell by your face."

"Shut up!" said Jennifer, close to tears again. "Can't you see I don't want to talk about it? And don't think *that* means there's anything to talk about. It was just a—a mirage. The way you see water shining on the highway on a hot day."

Jennifer turned away and began jogging down the hill, keeping far enough ahead of Robert so that he couldn't ask her any more questions.

They came down off the hillside onto the lane that led in one direction up to the Guthrie's place, and in the other down to the Taylor Farm and the main road. Robert went out to the road to wait for the bus, and Jennifer turned in to the farmhouse. She didn't renew her invitation to breakfast. If she had, Robert would have accepted this time. He wanted to be friends.

# chapter 2

When Jennifer walked into the dim kitchen, her mother was lighting a burner on the ancient gas stove in the corner. She jerked her hand back from the flaring blue flame and then subdued it with a heavy black kettle.

"Where on earth have you been?" she asked, looking around. Not giving Jennifer time to answer, she continued, "You're going to be late for school. If you must go out before breakfast, then I wish you would at least keep track of the time. How ever did you get so dirty?"

"I guess I'll need a bath before school," said Jennifer, looking at her dirty hands. The black soil of the moor was crusted under her fingernails. Suddenly Jennifer wanted to tell her mother about the strange thing she had seen at the standing stones, just so she could hear her mother say that she had imagined it all. But her mother's thoughts were elsewhere.

19

"A bath? Oh, Jennifer, I haven't got the wretched fire lit this morning, so there's no hot water. This is the day Mrs. Dean comes in to help, so I thought I'd let her do it."

The only way to heat water in the old farmhouse was to light the fire in the kitchen stove, pull out the damper, and wait for the water to circulate through a complex maze of pipes. To Mrs. Crandall's way of thinking it was all very primitive. Also, the fire was temperamental and usually just sat and sulked when she lit it, not quite going out, but never giving off enough heat to warm the water.

"You'll just have to wait for Mrs. Dean—she'll be here any minute—and then I'll drive you to school. Meantime you can have breakfast."

Mrs. Crandall reached up into a cupboard for the box of cornflakes and fetched the milk from the tiny refrigerator. By the time the kettle was boiling, Mrs. Dean came puffing into the kitchen. She went everywhere on an ancient bicycle and, despite the exercise, remained very stout. She untied her headscarf, patted her frizzy, gray hair into place, and hung her coat behind the door. She pulled a voluminous apron out of her purse and tied it around her ample waist.

"Well, what's there to do this morning?" she asked cheerfully.

"I thought maybe you could start with the fire," answered Mrs. Crandall. "I do wish there was some other way of heating the water."

"You'll be wanting one of them immerser heaters,"

said Mrs. Dean, shaking her head. "Extravagant things. With the price of electricity you're far better off with a coal fire. After all, it keeps the house cozy, and you can do the cooking on it, too, and save on the gas."

Cozy was the last word Mrs. Crandall would have used to describe the Taylor farmhouse, but Mrs. Dean soon had the fire roaring away like a furnace. Wiping her sooty hands on her apron, she accepted the cup of tea that Mrs. Crandall offered her and joined them at the table.

"Shouldn't you be away to school?" she asked Jennifer.

"She was out on the moor before breakfast and got herself dirty," said Mrs. Crandall. "She'll need a good wash first."

"You'll lose yourself out there on the moor," said Mrs. Dean disapprovingly. "It's not like you know your way around these parts."

"I wasn't alone," said Jennifer. "Robert Guthrie was with me."

"Robert Guthrie? That'll be Meg Guthrie's boy. The one that had polio when he was a wee lad. They say he never really got over it—always ailing—but his dad is bound and determined to make a farmer out of him."

"I don't believe I know Mrs. Guthrie," said Mrs. Crandall, looking thoughtful. "She doesn't come to the Institute meetings, does she? Or to the Friday whist games?"

Mrs. Crandall had entered into the village social life with great zeal.

"She keeps herself to herself, does Meg Guthrie," said Mrs. Dean. "Ever since Duncan left."

"Who is Duncan?" asked Jennifer.

Mrs. Dean stirred two spoonfuls of sugar into her tea and then willingly launched into the story of Duncan Guthrie. There was nothing she liked better than passing on a bit of gossip, and Mrs. Crandall made a good listener. Duncan was six years older than Robert, she told them, which would make him nearly seventeen now, but two years ago he had run away from home. Just disappeared one day and had never been heard of since. It had been hard on the Guthries because they set a lot of store by the boy.

"He was to get the farm when he grew up," she said. "But maybe that's where the trouble started. He was never all that keen on farming. More interested in motorbikes and cars. It was a motorbike that started all the trouble. He and another lad from Locharden stole a bike one day. They said they were just taking a spin on it and planned to put it back—that's as may be—but they wrecked it on the hill down to Baldry. The police found it and there was a real fuss, I can tell you!"

Mrs. Dean paused to sip her tea, then continued, "But boys will be boys, I say. His father and mother would have been better not to be so hard on him over it. After that they wouldn't let him have anything to do with any of the lads from the village. The only place he was allowed to go was school, and as it turned out he wasn't going there as often as he should. One day he just took off. Got himself a job somewhere, I suppose."

"And you say they've never heard from him?" asked Mrs. Crandall. "How dreadful for his poor parents."

"Aye, they really took it to heart. Meg Guthrie never comes to anything in the village now, and I hear they are awful strict with Robert, specially his dad. They make him work all the time—and him not strong—but I doubt if they'll make a farmer out of him, either. The lads aren't staying on the farms nowadays. It's the quick money in the cities or with the North Sea Oil they all want now."

She looked accusingly at Mrs. Crandall as if her husband's association with the North Sea Oil Company somehow made this her fault.

Mrs. Crandall shifted a little uncomfortably in her chair under Mrs. Dean's stare. "I should think the water is hot enough for your bath, Jennifer," she said brightly.

Jennifer, after gulping down the rest of her milk, ran off to check.

Robert had caught the bus to school, but for all the attention he paid to his lessons, he might as well not have been there. Mr. MacPherson droned on about the climate of India and then read a long poem by Sir Walter Scott. Robert stared down at his desk and thought about the stones. Why hadn't he, instead of Jennifer, seen those strange dark-haired people? He did not for one moment believe that she had imagined them.

During their morning break he looked for Jennifer but did not find her. After lunch he saw her playing soccer out in the field with the boys and, disregarding the game, he walked over to her and said, "What should we do about what happened at the stones?"

"What do you mean? What's there to do about it?" she asked, all the time keeping an eye on the ball, which was farther down the field.

"Maybe we should tell someone," said Robert.

"What's there to tell?" asked Jennifer and then added, "Look out! Here's the ball!"

Danny Lowrie came running down the field dribbling the ball, then passed it out to another player. He kept right on running and collided heavily with Robert, sending him sprawling on the grass.

"I thought you were supposed to be playing back," he said to Jennifer. "But maybe you'd rather baby-sit Guthrie!"

Jennifer looked down at Robert, half apologetic and half amused. Then, tossing back her long red hair, she went running off after the ball with Danny. Robert picked himself up and limped toward the school feeling angry and defeated.

Although the bell had not rung, Robert went into the classroom. One or two boys were there ahead of him and were crowded around the blackboard giggling. Robert paid no attention to them until one of them said, "Get Guthrie to draw him. He can do better than that."

"Hey, Robert," said a small sandy-haired boy. "Draw a picture o' Mr. MacPherson for us. Jimmy's drawing looks more like a scarecrow wi' glasses on!"

Robert might not have done it except that he had just been made to look silly by Danny Lowrie and rebuffed by Jennifer, and here was something he *could* do well. He took the chalk from Jimmy. The boys watched Robert with delight as he began to draw their teacher. It wasn't a kind picture—the eyes were beadier, the nose beakier, the hair tuftier, and the mouth more pulled down at the corners—but it *was* old MacPherson all right.

Robert was just adding a few final details when he was suddenly aware of the silence that had fallen in the room. No more giggles or encouraging remarks. The hair on the back of his neck prickled and, very slowly and reluctantly, he turned around to face the accusing glare of Mr. MacPherson. For just one second—before MacPherson shouted at him that he could stay after school for his impudence—Robert saw the hurt in the old man's eyes and wished that he had not done the drawing. Even after it was erased, a faint shadow of it remained on the board, looking down accusingly at him all afternoon.

He wished even more that he had not done it when

25

the rest of the children went home and Mr. MacPherson told him to take out his arithmetic book and work the problems on page 83—adding and subtracting meaningless fractions.

When, at last, Mr. MacPherson said that he could leave, he had missed the bus, and with it the chance to talk to Jennifer. He ran out, half hoping that she might have waited for him, but there was no one in sight, not even the usual stragglers on the soccer field.

As he trudged along the main road the grocery delivery van from Baldry stopped and gave him a lift. The van driver let him off at his road end, and as he passed the Taylor farm he noticed that the car was gone. Rather timidly he went up to the door and knocked. No one answered. Jennifer must have gone somewhere with her mother, he decided.

Disappointed at not seeing her, Robert plodded up the narrow lane. On one side was a drystone wall and on the other an overgrown hedge. Once, when he was much younger, a dog had jumped out at him from behind that hedge, and for a long time afterward he wouldn't go down the lane without Duncan. The place still reminded him of Duncan and how he had looked out for him—carrying his books home and not letting the other kids make fun of him when he wore that awful brace on his leg. Duncan couldn't have run away, leaving him behind, and never sending word for two long years.

Robert remembered when he had talked to his

grandfather about Duncan's disappearance the old man had said that he should seek an answer from the hills and the moor. He had also said that the answer to many things lay within the circle of stones. This brought Robert's thoughts back to the black-haired people Jennifer had seen. He picked up a rock and threw it angrily into the hedge, scaring out a scolding blackbird. Why couldn't *he* have seen these people?

By now Robert had reached the moor and could see his house ahead, a substantial stone farmhouse with a cluster of small outbuildings beside it. There was no garden to soften the grim lines of the building, and the paint on the door and window frames had weathered to a drab gray that matched the stone walls. Two straggly pine trees added to the desolate bleakness of the building.

Robert went around to the back, picking his way across the weedy yard, which was spattered with hen droppings. Before he reached the door, it was jerked open and his mother threw out a shower of potato peelings. The greedy hens came running, squawking.

When his mother caught sight of Robert, she called out, "There you are, at last, Robert. Where have you been?" Worry put a sharp edge on her voice. She had been regretting letting Robert go off so early to draw the stones, especially when he did not come home from school at his usual time.

"He'll have been playing along the way, wasting his time with other children, like as not," said a deeper voice from the kitchen.

Robert went inside, hanging his jacket on the back of the door and throwing his backpack onto the dresser.

"I'll be wanting you to go up on Ben Arden to see to the sheep."

"Aw, Dad, I'm tired," Robert protested.

"You're not too tired when it comes to playing with your friends instead of getting home to see what needs be done," said his father.

"Let the boy eat first," put in Mrs. Guthrie in a strained voice, and there was no more conversation until they were all seated around the table.

Mr. Guthrie was a short, heavy-set man with black hair and a weather-beaten face. He piled the mince and potatoes onto his plate and began to eat eagerly.

"How did the sale go, Dad?" Robert asked him after a while.

"Not so badly. Prices were up a little this year, so I made a bit on the lambs." Mr. Guthrie sounded quite amiable.

"Then it was worth going?"

"Aye. And I bought us a small pig to fatten up. Did you get the pigpen gate fixed while I was gone?"

Robert looked guilty. "It sort of slipped my mind," he said.

His father's good temper evaporated and he banged his fist on the table, making the dishes and silverware rattle. "Can you not do anything you're asked to do? Get outside and do it now!"

"Let the lad finish his supper," said Mrs. Guthrie.

"You just encourage him in his laziness," shouted her husband.

Robert got up from the table. It didn't matter that he hadn't finished his supper. Once the shouting started, he was never hungry.

He crossed the yard to the pigpen, which was a small enclosure built of stone with a roof of corrugated iron balanced over one corner. The hinge on the wooden gate was pulling away, and Robert saw that he would have to replace the board. He looked around the yard and sighed. The whole place seemed to be held together by scraps of wood and bits of wire.

There were some boards in a shed. Selecting one, he pulled out a few bent nails and measured it against the board on the gate. After sawing it to the right length, he began to pry the hinge off the old board.

"Hi there!"

Even without looking up, Robert recognized Jennifer's voice. He had been wanting to speak to her all day—but not here! Suppose his father came out of the house and started storming at him for wasting his time with his friends. Just thinking about it made him squirm. All the same, he was glad to see Jennifer because he was sure that this must mean that she was more concerned about what had happened that morning than she pretended to be.

"I've been thinking about the stone circle," Jennifer said, hitching herself up onto the corner of the pigpen roof, where she sat swinging her legs. "They say that seeing is believing, but I just can't believe that those people I saw were really there—yet it wasn't like a dream. I wish you'd seen them, too."

"Why couldn't they be real?" asked Robert.

"It stands to reason," said Jennifer. "I saw them digging in the ground as clearly as I see you hammering that board, but when you looked immediately after, there was no hole. I don't understand it."

"Just because you can't understand it doesn't mean that it's not real. There's lots of things you don't understand, and they're still real," argued Robert, pounding in a nail.

"Such as?"

"Well—television. Can you explain how, by turning on a switch, you can see people in your own living room that are doing things hundreds of miles away?"

"That's not the same at all," said Jennifer, tossing her head impatiently. "*I* can't explain television, but there are lots of people who can."

"Maybe my grandfather could explain what you saw," said Robert quietly.

"He couldn't make any more sense out of it than anyone else. I just imagined them."

"But people *have* disappeared there," Robert insisted.

"Name one! Just give me one name!"

30

"My brother—Duncan."

"Your brother Duncan didn't disappear," said Jennifer. "He ran away. Mrs. Dean said—"

"Mrs. Dean's an old gossip," shouted Robert, his eyes blazing.

"He stole a motorbike and was in trouble with the police."

"He did not! He only borrowed it. And he wouldn't run away. I know he wouldn't."

Robert and Jennifer glared at each other, red-faced and angry.

"You would believe anything, wouldn't you?" asked Jennifer.

"And you're too stupid to believe something even after you've seen it," Robert answered.

"And you're such a baby you believe in fairy stories that your grandpa tells you!"

While they were arguing Robert had finished replacing the hinge on the board. He was now struggling to hang the gate. Jennifer jumped down, intending to help him, but he ignored her.

"What did you come here for anyway?" he asked when he had finally maneuvered the gate into position.

A trace of a smile crossed Jennifer's face. "You won't believe this," she said, "but I came to ask you to go back to the stones with me."

"Back to the stones?" repeated Robert, looking at her blankly. "You mean you want to go back? But you keep saying you just imagined it all."

"Well," said Jennifer slowly, "I can't get those people out of my mind and I thought that if we went to the circle and nothing happened—and I don't think anything *will* happen—then it would be . . . finished."

"Maybe we should talk to my grandfather first," said Robert.

"You and your grandfather!" said Jennifer impatiently. "Do you want to go or not?"

From the house Robert could hear his father and mother arguing again, and he knew that Jennifer could hear them too.

"Yes. I'll come," he said quickly. "When?"

"Tomorrow morning," said Jennifer. "I want to get it over with. But we'll have to go really early—four o'clock. It's light by then. And Mom will be mad if I'm late for breakfast. She says she's fed up with me missing the bus."

"Where will I meet you?"

"On the road near my house where we cut off across the moor."

"I'll be there," Robert promised.

# chapter 3

From where Robert lay in bed he could see a patch of the night sky, pale and drained of color. It didn't get completely dark these midsummer nights, just a gray interval between dusk and dawn. Drifting through his mind were the half-remembered stories his grandfather used to tell him. The stories and his grandfather's cottage and the old man himself were not separate thoughts in Robert's mind. They had run together so that he could not remember one without the others.

The cottage, built of stone and roofed with thatch, crouched on the edge of the moor, looking out over the sands. Once, a whole village had stood between the house and the sea, but his grandfather said it had been swallowed up by the sands, just as the sands had swallowed up his field, and would one day claim his house. Robert had seen the sands moving when the wind was from the east. Drifts of fine sand waited on the doorstep and the windowsill, and little ripples crept under the door.

Sitting on a low stool at his grandfather's feet, beside a sweet-smelling peat fire, Robert had listened to the old man tell stories of the days before the village had been overtaken by sand, and of times when the Stones of Arden marched to the sea. It was but a small step in belief from the shifting sands to the walking stones.

On rare occasions, the great stones of Arden would drape themselves in mist and leave their place on the moor to march northeastward and stand on a clifftop high above the sea. Anyone who came near the marching stones was caught up in the folds of mist and lost in time.

It was the uncanny resemblance between Jennifer's experience and this memory of his grandfather's story that made him think that he should go and see the old man before they went back to the stones. But the trouble was, he couldn't be absolutely sure that his grandfather would be of any help. The old man lived in Baldry now, in that bare little council house given to him when his own house was declared unfit to live in, and it seemed to Robert that his stories had been left behind with everything else he cared about in the old house.

The sky was now faintly streaked with pink. Robert wondered if Jennifer would really show up. He, himself, was a little nervous about sneaking out. But if anything *did* happen at the stones, it would make a fine tale to tell his grandfather. It would give the old man something new to think about.

Robert climbed out of bed, pulled on his clothes, and crept downstairs. Taking a page from a school exercise book, he scribbled a note to his father: "Have gone up on Ben Arden to check the sheep before going to school." There! That should satisfy him. Hadn't the whole fuss last night started because his father wanted him to check the sheep?

The chill, damp air struck Robert when he stepped outside. Turning up the collar of his jacket and thrusting his hands into his pockets, he hurried down the road. Soon he could see the hawthorn hedge, ragged and black, that marked the boundary between the fields and the moor. Slowly, a dark figure detached itself from the blackness of the hedge, and when he was close enough he saw that it was Jennifer.

"You're here!" said Robert. "I wasn't sure you'd want to get up this early two mornings in a row."

"Of course I'm here. I was afraid *you* wouldn't come," said Jennifer. "This is exciting! The whole world seems different—sort of new—this early in the morning."

They struck off across the moor, following a faintly discernible path that had been made by sheep. Like the sheep, they had to walk single file, so there was little chance to talk; anyway, they were both busy with their own thoughts. Robert saw no sign of the sheep on that side of Ben Arden, but he decided that it would be easier to look for them on the way back when the light was better. Besides, it was unlikely that they would be that far west on the mountain.

They reached the crest of the shoulder of Ben Arden and, far below them, they could see the circle of stones. The sun had come up, flooding the sky with color and shining on the distant sea.

"Let's go!" Jennifer's voice rang out as she went bounding down the short turf on the hillside. Robert, affected by her high spirits, went running down the hill after her. A bird exploded from the ground under Jennifer's feet and she stopped with a cry of fright.

"It's just a grouse!" said Robert, laughing at her panic. "There are lots of them on the moor."

"I knew what it was," said Jennifer resentfully. "I just hadn't expected it."

She slowed down to a walk because they had reached the bracken, which grew thick and tall as a jungle on that side of the hill. They had completely lost sight of their goal, and when they came down onto the flat they were in marshy ground and had to retrace their steps more than once. They were both growing tired.

"How much farther?" asked Jennifer.

"On the other side of that rise," said Robert.

They climbed the rise and there stood the stone circle ahead of them, solemn and somehow threatening.

"What should we do now that we're here?" Jennifer asked nervously as they approached the stones.

"We dig down and find the fallen stones like we did yesterday," answered Robert.

Today their roles were reversed. Jennifer was still the unbeliever, yet she was the more frightened. Robert believed, but was willing to test the unknown. Reluctantly, Jennifer knelt down between the stones and began to dig with her hands. The dirt came away easily where it had been roughly pushed into place the day before. Robert knelt in the other gap, with the stone between them, and began to tear up handfuls of peat and roots. A lark sang in the sky, high above them, and behind them they heard the plaintive call of a curlew.

The mist gathered slowly, just a faint coolness and dampness around the stones and fragile wisps above the ground that came together and then disappeared. Then Robert noticed the silence. The clear song of the lark and the harsher cry of the moor bird were stilled. When he looked up he saw that fog now blanketed the ground within the circle of stones. Jennifer was just a gray shadow of herself, still digging down toward the hidden slab of rock.

The coldness of the fog soaked into Robert, numbing his limbs, and with each breath he could feel it penetrating deep inside him. His hands were scraping against the rock and he suddenly wanted to push the soil back into the hole that he had dug, covering up the stone that he had found, but the cold seemed to

37

have reached his brain and he had no more power over his thoughts. Gradually the numbing cold was replaced by the soothing warmth of the sun, and the oppressive silence was broken by a sound that he could not at first identify. And then he knew what it was. It was the sound of waves breaking on the shore.

Jennifer had stopped digging and was standing near him. Her eyes had that same unfocused, frightened look that Robert had noticed in them the day before. Both she and Robert looked across the circle to the place where the third stone was missing. The fog was dissolving, melting away in the sunshine, and they could see that they were no longer alone. Kneeling between the stones, digging down into the ground, was a black-haired boy.

"What has happened? Where are we?" Jennifer whispered.

Robert looked around. Nothing was as it had been before. The endless moor around them had been replaced by a thick growth of trees and bushes that looked like great, overgrown rhododendrons—dark and gloomy—pressing in around the stone circle.

"What's happened?" asked Jennifer again.

"Listen!" said Robert. "What do you hear?"

"Nothing," said Jennifer, her blue eyes darting anxiously about. "Just the leaves rattling on those horrid dark bushes."

"Don't you hear the sea? You can never hear the

sea from the Stones of Arden, no matter what direction the wind."

"So what?" asked Jennifer.

"Don't you see what that means? The stones have moved, like my grandfather said. We're caught in the mists of time."

"We can't be," said Jennifer. Yet the only things familiar in the entire landscape were the ten standing stones with the gaps for three more between.

Robert walked quietly across the short grass that carpeted the middle of the circle toward the boy who was kneeling in the other gap. Thinking about it afterward, Robert was surprised that he had approached the boy with so little fear, but there was nothing intimidating about the boy as he saw him there, crouched on the ground.

When Robert was close to him he saw that he was wrapped in some sort of blanket or cloak of gray wool. Jennifer had joined Robert, and it was only when her shadow fell across the boy that he became aware of their presence. He jumped up, obviously startled, and turned to face them.

He had long black hair and a lean, tanned face with prominent cheekbones and very dark eyes fringed by long lashes. There were tears on his cheeks. Now that he was standing they could see that under his cloak he wore a gray tuniclike garment, richly embroidered, and loose trousers.

The boy's eyes flickered over them. Robert wondered if their jeans and jackets looked strange to him. Then he asked in a high voice, oddly accented and curiously calm, considering his words, "Who are you? Have you come to kill me, too?"

"We're not going to hurt you," said Robert, his voice hoarse and nervous, giving away his own fear, so that the boy should have been reassured. "Why would you think that?"

"Are you not with the Barbaric Ones from across the sea—the people who killed my Chosen Brother, Aetherix?"

"We don't know anything about them," said Robert, looking nervously around. He didn't like the way the boy kept talking of killing in his strange, calm voice.

The boy turned to Jennifer and reached out as if to touch her, but she backed away. "Are you two of the Lost Ones?" he asked.

Jennifer just stared at him, but Robert echoed the words. "The Lost Ones," he said. "Maybe we are lost."

In the short silence that followed his words, Robert was again aware of the sound of the surf close by. "Can you tell me how near we are to the sea?" he asked.

"You come from across the sea?" asked the boy, suddenly suspicious again.

"No," said Robert. "You really don't need to be frightened of us. Honestly we won't hurt you. You see, we need *your* help. We're lost and I think it has something to do with these stones—though I suppose that sounds impossible to you."

"With the Circle of Time?" asked the boy.

"Is that what you call it?" Why do you call it that?"

"It is old. It has seen the rise and fall of many civilizations, the coming and going of many people."

"Does it ever move?" asked Robert.

"Move? You mean the stones move? How could they?"

"I can hear waves breaking, but the stones are a long way from the sea."

The boy shook his head. "There is only a narrow strip of bushes between us here and the top of the cliff above the sea. But surely it is easier to believe that the sea could move than these stones."

Jennifer, who had been listening in frightened silence, began to cry. "I don't like this. I want to get away from here."

The boy looked concerned, and apparently forgetting his own unhappiness, said, "Come over to the other side of the circle and you shall share my meal-bread and tell me where you came from."

They crossed the circle and sat down together beside one of the stones. The boy reached into a pocket in his tunic and brought out a small package wrapped in leaves and opened it. In it were several small flat cakes.

"Before we eat together, we must know each other's names. I am Kartan."

"I'm Robert, and she's Jennifer."

"Robert, Jennifer," Kartan repeated, handing each of them one of the cakes.

"Maybe we'd better not eat it," Jennifer whispered to Robert. "It looks weird."

"It looks just like an oatcake," Robert answered, embarrassed by Jennifer's tactlessness. "What's it made from?"

"It is our mealbread made from ground nuts and honey and flour and dried fruit. We take it with us on our journeys and it banishes hunger for many hours. There is not much to eat in these woods."

Robert took a bite and found that the mealbread's nutty flavor was more appetizing than its appearance.

"It's really good," he told Jennifer reassuringly. She nibbled hers cautiously.

"What sort of journey are you on?" Jennifer asked between bites.

"Our summer journey," answered Kartan. "We explore the Northlands every summer looking for artifacts of the past, and for the Lost Ones."

"Artifacts? Lost Ones?" Robert repeated.

"I can't get what you're talking about," said Jennifer. "It's like we came into the middle of a movie. There doesn't seem to be a beginning. You were here, in this stone circle, digging for artifacts?"

"No," answered Kartan. "There is little to be found here. Most of our artifacts come from the old city of Norsea which stands as it did before the floods."

"What floods?" asked Robert.

"The floods of a hundred years ago. You cannot be ignorant of the years of the Great Floods," said Kartan in surprise. "When the ice caps melted and the sea level rose."

"When the ice caps melted?" Robert repeated in a bewildered tone.

"I never heard of any floods in the nineteenth century," said Jennifer.

"The twenty-first century," Kartan corrected her quietly. The blank fear he saw reflected in their eyes made him hesitate for a moment before he added, "This is the year 2179."

The mealbread fell from Jennifer's fingers and she gave a choking cry. Robert said slowly, "Lost in the mists of time. But I never thought it would be in the future—it would have been easier, somehow, to be part of the past."

"What are you saying?" asked Kartan, still curiously calm. "You mean that you are from the past?"

The question hung in the air for a long time. Then Robert answered, "From two hundred years ago. How can we get back?"

There was a great deal that Kartan wanted to know, but Robert and Jennifer were so confused by the enormity of what had happened that they seemed unable to understand even the most straightforward question. Finally, Kartan broke through to them, saying, "We must not stay here much longer in case the Barbaric Ones come back."

"Who *are* the Barbaric Ones?" Robert asked.

"They are a wild people from across the sea who attacked us while we were traveling here in the Far Northlands. They have taken some of our people as prisoners, and even those who escaped are still followed by the Barbaric Ones and may not reach home. I was with those who escaped, but I came back here to the grave of Aetherix. It is hard to be parted from a Chosen One."

"The Barbaric Ones killed him?" Robert asked.

"And some of your people buried him here?" asked Jennifer.

Kartan nodded.

"It's what I saw before," she said to Robert. She sounded almost reassured, as if there might be some pattern or sequence to these strange events after all. "I told you it was a grave. So I *did* see something."

"But that was three days ago," said Kartan. "Have you been here all that time?"

Jennifer shook her head, then asked, "What are *you* doing here if that was three days ago?"

"I came back because I wanted to bury a painting near Aetherix—a painting of the stones that he loved."

Kartan gestured to the stones as he spoke, and Jennifer noticed that the knuckles of his right hand were scraped and raw.

"How did you do that?" she asked.

"I hit a rock under the soil when I was digging."

Turning to Robert, Jennifer said excitedly, "The

44

third fallen stone! He was digging over there where the missing stone should stand."

Robert looked around at the circle of tall stones. The Circle of Time, Kartan had called it. Ten standing stones and three lost under the earth and roots. The stones, the mists, the half-remembered legends. He was struggling to piece together these fragmented thoughts when a slight movement among the bushes across the circle, near where they had first seen Kartan kneeling, attracted Robert's attention. A bearded face peered around one of the stones.

"Someone's watching us!" he said.

Kartan spun around. Jumping up, he dodged behind the nearest stone and ran into the dark woods, shouting, "Run! Run! It's one of them. One of the Barbaric Ones."

# chapter 4

Robert hesitated for only a second, just long enough to see a large, swarthy, dark-haired man spring from behind the stone into the circle, and then he plunged into the trees after Jennifer and Kartan.

The rhododendron wood was very dark. The great canopy of thick leaves above them shut out the sun so that no plants or flowers grew on the forest floor. The damp, peaty soil was covered with fallen leaves —large, leathery brown leaves—that rustled and crackled underfoot. In their headlong flight they snapped off twigs and broke branches, and the noise of the chase seemed to spread through the awful silence like black footprints on new-fallen snow.

Robert's heart was pounding so hard, partly from fear and partly from the exertion of running, that he began to feel dizzy. The muscles of his right leg, which had remained weak since his illness, seemed to have been replaced by foam rubber, and he knew that he could not run much farther. Jennifer and Kartan were well ahead of him now, running easily, dodging through the trees, ducking beneath low branches. Close behind him he could hear the heavy tread and wheezing breath of his pursuer—the Barbaric One. That thought forced him to try and run faster, but one leg seemed to get in the way of the other. With a cry of panic, he fell to the ground.

The Barbaric One was on him, grunting and talking in a strange guttural language that Robert could not understand. Robert offered no resistance when the man roughly pinned his arms behind his back and tied his wrists with some sort of thin cord that bit into his skin. Then Robert was jerked to his feet and stood there swaying slightly. To his surprise, he saw that Kartan was walking back through the trees, apparently intending to give himself up and be taken prisoner also.

"It will be better for you if we are together," Kartan said quietly to Robert.

Before he could say more, the bearded man jumped forward and struck Kartan on the side of the head and then tied Kartan's wrists behind his back. The man stood for a moment, peering into the trees, as if expecting that Jennifer might come back also, but there was no sign of her. Only silence. The intensity of the silence—no birdsong, no rustling leaves, no hum of insects, no distant voices—gave the place a sinister, unreal quality. It was almost a relief when the huge man indicated with a jerk of his head that they were to come with him, and the sound of their scuffling footsteps covered up the waiting quiet.

Robert kept tripping over roots and stumbling into hollows and dips that were concealed by the leaves covering the ground. With his hands tied behind him, he found it difficult to keep his balance, and he had no means of pushing low branches out of the way. But he was almost unaware of these difficulties because of the turmoil of his thoughts. If only he had been able to run faster. Why had Kartan come back to help him like that, yet had offered no resistance when the man caught him? And what had happened to Jennifer? They should have stayed together. Would Jennifer try to follow them? Or would she go back to the stones and maybe get back to their own time. Then what would happen to *him*—would he be left here forever?

They had not gone far when the trees ended abruptly and they emerged on a clifftop high above the sea. Robert stood there, blinking at the brightness of the sun dancing on the waves below him. This was not a stretch of the coast he recognized. Two spurs of rock extended raggedly out into the water enclosing a small bay. Three boats were anchored close to shore, and several men were dragging drift-wood along the beach as if to start a fire.

The Barbaric One cut the cords that bound their wrists and motioned to them to go down a path cut into the cliff. The path dropped away so steeply that Robert had not even noticed it, and he hung back until the man pushed him forward with a torrent of angry words.

Kartan went first and, apparently aware that Robert was afraid, helped him as best he could from below, while the man shouted at them from above —or perhaps he shouted to someone down on the beach. Robert could not be sure because all his concentration was centered on getting down the vertical cliff.

"There's a foothold a little to the right," Kartan said, guiding Robert's foot. "Watch out for this big rock! It's loose!"

Robert inched his way down cautiously, clinging tightly wherever there were handholds because he was unable to trust any weight on his right leg. Seeing Kartan scramble down ahead of him so easily and leap lightly down to the beach below produced a familiar feeling of resentment at his own clumsiness.

When Robert finally felt firm sand below his feet, he looked back along the cliff and saw, some distance away, the wide, black entrance to a cave. Lounging beside it were two more men, one tall and thin, with light-colored hair, and the other dark and bearded. They came over to the boys and seized them roughly, then dragged them to the cave and pushed them inside.

Robert, his eyes adjusted to the brightness of the beach, could at first see nothing when he stared into the cave, but rustling sounds and whispering voices told him there were other people in there. Then a high, echoing voice exclaimed, "It is Kartan! And he brings someone with him."

"Savotar!" said Kartan, reaching out into the darkness. "Can that really be you? Are you all safe? How many are here?"

A crowd of twelve or fifteen people, all with brown skin and straight black hair like Kartan's, surged forward into the light at the mouth of the cave. One man, taller than the others, wore a long robe of shimmering material, while the others were dressed in gray tunics and trousers, many with gray woolen cloaks over their shoulders.

"Who is this with you?" asked the tall man. "Is he one of their children?"

"No, he is not one of them, Savotar," Kartan answered. "He is called Robert. We met at the stone circle. There is a girl, too, called Jennifer."

"Where is she?" The question was asked by a woman with a gentle voice, who wore her long hair braided and coiled over her ears.

"We are not sure, Nemourah," answered Kartan. "One of the Barbaric Ones chased us and Jennifer escaped."

"But where have they come from? Can they be two of the Lost Ones?"

"I do not really understand how they came here. We have had little time to talk."

"What news do you have of the rest of our people?" Savotar asked Kartan. "Are they still pursued by the Barbaric Ones? Tell us all that you know. We have been captive here for three days, and are without news of what has been happening."

The people gathered around Kartan and, sitting cross-legged on the sandy ground near the entrance to the cave, waited for him to speak. It reminded Robert of story time at school when he was younger. Rather awkwardly, he crouched down beside them.

"Three days ago," began Kartan. "I went with some of our people to gather driftwood on the shore, and we were surprised to see boats anchored out in the bay. There was no one about, but we found the remains of a fire and saw that people had slept here, in this cave, where we planned to spend the night. At once we feared that the Barbaric Ones had returned.

"We talked together and decided to go to the Circle of Time to hold council with you, Savotar, and with Edomerid. We also wanted to warn the rest of our people, but when we got there we found that we were already too late. We found the body of my brother, Aetherix."

Kartan's voice shook and he was unable to continue for some time. The people waited in comforting silence.

"We dug a grave and buried him there where we had found him."

Robert nodded. The scene that Jennifer had witnessed.

"While we were there we were joined by more

of our people. They had seen the killing of Aetherix. They said that he had fought with the Barbaric Ones and that you and Nemourah and the others had been captured. In spite of Aetherix's death, it does not seem that the Barbaric Ones mean to kill us—just take us captive. They are still wandering about, searching out our people, tracking them through the forest. I am afraid that they may follow them all the way to Kelso where Vianah and the children await us."

"Our people would not knowingly lead them there," said an older man.

"Suppose they do not know they are being followed?"

"Why had you stayed at the circle?" Savotar asked Kartan. "Were you there alone?"

"I escaped with Alloperla and Panchros and was on my way back to Kelso with them, but the pain of leaving Aetherix was great. I wanted to bury one of his paintings near him, so I returned to the grave. That is where Robert and Jennifer found me."

"Who are these Barbaric Ones, and why do they want to capture you?" Robert asked, his curiosity finally overcoming his shyness.

"They come from across the sea. We call them the Barbaric Ones because they have retained the ways of people who lived long ago. They are interested in wealth and machines and factories, but the sources of energy and raw materials to sustain such a way of life are almost gone. Now they are going to exploit people to meet their needs."

"What do you mean?" asked Robert.

Nemourah took up the story, and her gentle voice made the words she spoke all the more terrible. "They plan to take us back to their country in these boats anchored out in the bay, but they want more of us, so we are being held prisoner in this cave until they have captured the rest of our people. They will force us to do the work of some of their machines, and to dig coal from the deepest mines to make electricity to keep their factories and machinery working."

"You mean . . . we'll be slaves?" Robert asked in a terrified whisper.

"In spite of their technology they are ignorant people," said Savotar. "They compare our life with theirs, and because we have not many possessions, they think that we are losing nothing by leaving this land. Yet our people, who have adapted to the new ways, are more fortunate than those who cling to a past that is gone."

"How can you be sure about this?" Robert asked, clutching at straws. "They don't even talk our language. You can't really know."

"Many years ago they captured several of our men, who then lived with the Barbaric Ones for a long time," explained Savotar. "They finally escaped and returned to our people, bringing back with them the knowledge of their ways and understanding of

53

their language. As time passed, we began to hope that the Barbaric Ones had forgotten us and were going to leave us in peace, but now they find they need us to do their work."

"Can't we escape?" asked Robert, looking around wildly.

"The only way is to take the steep path up the cliff," said Savotar. "They would see us."

"Couldn't we overpower them or something?" suggested Robert. "I have seen only six of them—there are far more of us."

"It is not a question of numbers," said Savotar. "They are armed, and our people have not fought for generations. We believe in peace. We cannot allow ourselves to revert to the ways of primitive peoples who meet violence with violence."

"But you can't just do *nothing*," said Robert. He wasn't keen on fighting either, but he couldn't see being taken into slavery without putting up some sort of resistance.

"We may yet be saved," said Savotar calmly. "Love and trust are more powerful than violence and hate. We will not fight. Aetherix, the Chosen Brother of Kartan, fought in anger when he saw one of the Barbaric Ones ill-treating Nemourah. They killed Aetherix, and his death brought greater pain to Nemourah than the Barbaric One's cruelty did."

"I don't see that it would have been right for him to stand there and do nothing," said Robert stubbornly.

"It takes real courage to hold back anger. Aetherix had none of that kind of courage—only anger," answered Savotar. "What use is it for us to believe that trust, love, and sharing are real forces in the world, only to abandon that belief when we need it most?"

Robert couldn't find words to express his thoughts. What kind of courage was it for them to sit here in this cave doing nothing, accepting the loss of the way of life they believed in?

"Come!" said Savotar soothingly, as if sensing Robert's frustration. "Let us share mealbread together."

They passed around small portions of mealbread and a jug of water. Robert sat in silence, staring out of the cave, and this time the mealbread was as tasteless as sawdust. He felt tired, dragged down by all that had happened in such a short space of time.

He was trapped inside concentric circles. He must escape from the Barbaric Ones, escape from Kartan's people, escape from this point in time. And what about Jennifer? Had she eluded the clutches of the Barbaric One, only to be left wandering alone in that dark, silent forest? How was he ever to find her again?

# chapter 5

The evening was calm and warm. Waves lapped against the shore as the three boats out in the bay rose and fell in the gentle swell. Farther down the beach six men sat around a roaring fire.

The idea that they were prisoners of these men, and that the boats were waiting to carry them off to slavery, seemed utterly impossible to Robert. He closed his eyes tightly, sure that when he opened them again he would find that the whole confused happening had been a dream. But when he opened his eyes, everything remained the same, and he found that Kartan was staring at him curiously.

"Why have you come to us?" Kartan asked quietly.

"I don't know how I got here," said Robert. "*I* didn't make this happen—I can tell you that."

"Hush!" said Kartan, looking nervously back into

the cave. "It is better that the others do not know about you yet."

"But they *do* know," said Robert.

"They accept you as one of the Lost Ones. They do not yet know that you come from the past. They do not know that you are like Vianah's children."

"Vianah's children?" repeated Robert.

Once again he had the feeling of being sucked into a quagmire of facts that made no sense.

"Don't you know Vianah's children? Ollie and Ian and the others?" This time it was Kartan's turn to be puzzled. "When I found that you had come from their time I was sure that you must have something to do with them—or with Vianah."

"Nothing you say makes sense," said Robert in a tired voice. "You might as well talk the same language as these Barbaric Ones for all the sense you make."

"I will tell you from the beginning," said Kartan, assuming the slightly singsong voice he had used when he told the story of being chased by the Barbaric Ones. "Last year we left Vianah behind in an old tower near our town of Kelso when we went on our summer journey. Vianah is the oldest of our people and is almost blind; the journey was too difficult for her. We left her with a supply of mealbread and fuel and water, but we were gone longer than we had intended, and when we returned Vianah had used up all the food that we had left. But she did not starve. Four children came to her. They had names that are strange to our ears—Elinor, Andrew, Ian, and Ollie. Stranger than their names was the fact that they came from a world where people traveled in cars and flew in airplanes and had even walked on the moon. They came out of long ago."

"What year did they come from?" asked Robert.

"I do not think they told Vianah—or she did not tell me. Two of them traveled through the woods back to Kelso and brought Vianah food from our people's gardens. They built a fire to warm her and made soup. She says that without their help she would not have lived."

"Did you see them?" asked Robert.

"They left before we returned. They went back to their own time."

"How?" asked Robert. "How did they get back?"

To Robert this was the most interesting part of the whole story, but Kartan just shrugged. Vianah had not told him, and he had not thought to ask.

"If you never saw them, then how can you be sure that she wasn't making it all up? After all, *she* didn't see them either if she is blind."

"I saw the basket of peaches."

"Peaches?"

"When we left on our journey the peaches were not ripe, but when we returned there was a basket of peaches beside Vianah in the tower. She could not have walked to Kelso by herself. Someone brought them to her. Besides, Vianah told me, so it is true. She liked to tell of them to me and to Lara Avara, her Chosen One."

"Who are these Chosen Ones you keep talking about?" Robert asked.

Kartan looked blankly at Robert for a moment, and then said, "Of course! In your time each family lived by itself. We choose the people we live with."

"Like in a commune?" Robert asked.

Kartan wrinkled his brow, unable to understand Robert's question. "If we can just escape from here, then I will take you to Kelso to meet my Chosen Ones."

Kartan's words brought a flicker of hope to Robert. Here, at last, was someone talking of escape.

"I have read some history of your time," Kartan continued. "People killed great numbers of their enemies with bombs and guns. Perhaps *you* could frighten away the Barbaric Ones."

"Don't be stupid!" protested Robert, irritated by the uselessness of Kartan's idea. "Boys don't run around with bombs and guns in their pockets. All I've got is a scout knife. Besides, if your people don't believe in violence, they can't expect me to take on the Barbaric Ones single-handed."

"There must be a reason for so great a thing as your coming. These others came to Vianah in her time of need. Surely you have come to save our people from the Barbaric Ones." Kartan turned and looked at Robert with dark, pleading eyes.

59

Robert was engulfed in a rising tide of panic. Saving himself, and maybe Jennifer, was more than he could cope with, and now here was Kartan, so quiet and assured, asking him to save all his people from slavery. Robert wanted to jump up and run across the beach screaming and shouting. That would bring the guards running. They were apparently pretty sure of Kartan's people the way they were sitting around the fire as if it were a picnic or something. Why couldn't Kartan's people just creep out? What was needed was a diversion to occupy the guards while they all climbed the cliff.

Robert raised his eyes to the three boats quietly bobbing about in the bay. The boats! A plan was beginning to form in his mind. He thrust his hand into his pocket and felt for his knife. It had a good, strong steel blade.

"How do you suppose these boats are anchored?" he asked Kartan.

"With ropes and weights," answered Kartan.

"With ropes or wire?" Robert asked urgently. "With rope that I could cut with this knife?" He pulled out his knife and flicked out the blade.

Kartan didn't answer the question, lost in admiration of Robert's knife. "We could ask Savotar—but why do you need to know?"

"If I cut the anchor rope on one of the boats, it should drift toward those rocks. When the guards see that happening, they will go out to save it—after all, they need the boats. While they are busy down there, you can all sneak out and climb up the cliff."

"But how can you reach the boats unseen? To get to them you would need to go past the guards."

"I'll go along the top of the beach close to the cliff, then cross the sand behind those rocks over there."

Robert pointed to a spur of rock that stretched darkly from the foot of the cliff right out to the sea. It would be a long swim from where the rocks met the water out to the boats, right across in front of the Barbaric Ones.

"Could you swim so far?" Kartan asked anxiously.

Robert knew that Kartan was thinking about how he had been caught so easily in the woods, and had been afraid to climb down the cliff, but swimming was something he was good at. After having polio he had gone to the swimming pool in Baldry for therapy. In the water he never felt clumsy and slow, and he was quite sure he could swim out to the boats, provided there were no strong currents or tides. And he wouldn't know that until he was out there.

"Let us speak of your plan to the others," said Kartan.

The idea of meeting the calm, curious eyes of all these brown-skinned people did not appeal to Robert at all, but Kartan had already moved farther into the cave and was telling them about the plan in a slow, singsong voice.

"I can only cut rope, not wire," said Robert, when Kartan was describing his knife.

"I am sure that it will be rope," said Savotar. "Metal is in such short supply that it is reserved for uses for which there is no substitute. I am more concerned with the risk that you, yourself, are taking."

"He cannot be allowed to do this," said Nemourah quietly. "It will only result in anger and violence."

"Not if you sneak quietly away while they're out there saving their boat," said Robert.

"He came to help us," Kartan pleaded earnestly.

"Where did he come from?" asked a voice from the back of the group.

"He came out of the past," said Kartan.

That's done it, thought Robert. They'll never get back to deciding on anything now. But to his surprise, they accepted this incomprehensible piece of news more calmly than the idea of Robert cutting loose the boat.

Talk swirled around Robert, and he lost track of what was being said in these high voices until he was suddenly aware that Savotar was saying to him formally, "You will go now, protected by your love and concern for us."

Robert shuffled uncomfortably at these words. "Maybe I shouldn't go until it's completely dark."

"It would be better to go now," answered Kartan. "Soon the moon will be up, shining on the water, and then they would be sure to see you."

Robert felt some of his daring ebb away.

"I don't think it's dark enough," he insisted.

"They will not see you in the shadow of the cliff, and they are not expecting trouble from the sea," Kartan assured him.

It had been one thing to talk about it. It was another to do it. Yet, Robert felt a sense of relief as he slipped out of the cave and began to creep along the base of the cliff. Reaching the boats at least required action, which was better than sitting there in the cave trying to sort out all his conflicting thoughts and emotions.

He breathed in the strong iodine smell of the seaweed at the high-water mark and heard the soft, sucking sound of the waves on the sand. The smells and sounds reminded him of the beach near his grandfather's cottage. He wriggled down the sand, making sure that he remained well hidden by the rocks.

Robert was, in fact, observed as he crawled down the sand toward the sea behind the spur of rock. He was being watched from the top of the cliff by none other than Jennifer, although she was too far away to be absolutely sure who he was.

When the Barbaric One had startled them in the stone circle, Jennifer's one thought had been to run. She had dashed for the cover of the wood and, in her panic, had not remembered that Robert could not run very fast. She had bolted like a frightened animal, wanting only to put distance between her and the bearded giant who was chasing them.

When, at last, she was too tired and short of breath to run any farther, she paused and looked around. To her alarm she found that she was quite alone in the wood. This discovery frightened her almost as much as being chased. After standing still for a minute, listening to the empty silence, she began to shout Robert's name. But her shout was absorbed into the leafy stillness. Although she strained her ears, she could hear neither an answering shout nor the sound of footsteps. Had they taken some other route through the forest, she wondered? Or had they been caught by that awful man? Surely she would have heard their screams if that had happened.

She stood still, considering both possibilities, and it was then that she really became aware of how quiet it was. It was as if she were the only living thing for miles around, as if every other creature was under some strange enchantment. The silence unnerved her. And then there was the merest whisper of sound. Somewhere behind her, a breeze rattled a leaf, and Jennifer spun around in alarm. She imagined little creatures creeping up on her, creatures invisible in the dim light. It was, in fact, only the first stirrings of the evening breeze, but for Jennifer the dim forest was full of sinister whispers and the glint of hostile eyes. Then the wind dropped again, and the silence came back, and she was not sure that that wasn't even worse.

She tried to retrace her steps, but in every direction the trees looked the same. It was a strange, featureless place with no paths, no stumps, no streams, and no open spaces. Only endless, dusty limbs and thick, dark leaves. The rustle of the dry leaves under her feet sounded like someone following her. She stopped and looked back, half hopeful and half afraid; but there was no one there, only the awful silence.

Although Robert had been frightened and bewildered by what had happened to them he was not nearly as unprepared as Jennifer. All his life he had listened to the tales his grandfather told, and some of the mystery and feeling of this place was in his blood. But for Jennifer the unexpectedness of it was completely overwhelming. Her only goal was to find the stone circle and get back to where she belonged—where she was in command. She didn't even read books that had a hint of unreality in them. No falling down rabbit holes or pushing through the back of a wardrobe for her—yet here she was, trapped in this terrible place.

Suddenly the whole thing made her angry. She was angry that Robert had got her here, angry with the boy Kartan for deserting her, and angry that reality had let her down.

She had no idea how long she had been wandering in the wood. It was becoming darker but, because she could not see the sky, she was not sure if night was coming or if the day had clouded over. Maybe the wood was just denser, the leaves thicker.

Also, she was hungry. There was absolutely nothing to eat unless the leathery leaves were edible. There was no undergrowth, not even mushrooms or moss. Not that she would have dared to eat mushrooms, especially here. She had seen no streams and, thinking of that, she discovered she was thirsty, unbearably thirsty. She had to get out of this wood before she died of hunger or thirst or loneliness. She thought maybe loneliness would get her first.

Then she heard a sound different from the scuffing leaves. It was the sound of the sea.

This discovery brought her new hope. If she could just reach the sea, she would be free from this awful wood. The forest itself had changed somewhat. The ground was now carpeted with moss and short grass, and the trees were different—less dense and forbidding—and some tree quite near filled the air with heavy perfume. Then the wood ended altogether, very abruptly. Jennifer found that she was on a cliff, high above the sea, out on a point, looking back on the wide sweep of a bay.

Perhaps the greatest relief of all was to see people down on the beach sitting around a fire. She was so excited to find that she was no longer completely alone in the world that she wanted to shout to them, to ask them to help her down. But caution reasserted itself. Suppose they were the Barbaric Ones the boy had spoken of? Maybe she shouldn't attract their attention.

There were three boats out in the bay, boats that looked like long rowboats. The men must have come ashore in these boats, she thought, because she could, at first, see no way down the cliff; but on examining the whole curve of the cliff she saw that farther around there was a rough path, though she wasn't sure that she would dare to venture down it. Near the bottom of the path was the dark mouth of a cave and, more interesting than that, two people were sitting at the entrance. It was too dark to be sure, but she thought they could easily have been Robert and Kartan.

This puzzled her. Were the people around the fire the Barbaric Ones? And, if so, why did Robert and Kartan not keep out of sight? Were they waiting until it was completely dark before trying to escape up the cliff? She settled down to watch.

The sun had dropped behind the trees so that it was hard to see the boys at all. Then, just as Jennifer was giving up hope of anything happening, she saw a slight movement. One of the boys began to edge along the bottom of the cliff—not toward the path as she had expected, but in the opposite direction. When he was beyond a ridge of rock he ran down the sand to the water's edge.

She could see him distinctly against the light-colored sand, but he would be hidden by rocks from the men on the beach. His loping run convinced her that it was Robert, and she wondered what on earth he was doing. Then, when he stripped off his pants and sweater and wriggled down to the sea, she understood his plan.

He was going to swim out to the boats and escape

from the Barbaric Ones that way. Instead of going back to the woods to look for her, he was intent on saving his own skin by making away with one of their boats. Jennifer bit down hard on her lower lip, fighting back tears, then tossed her red hair back in a defiant gesture. Robert had got her into this mess, but apparently she was on her own now. She couldn't count on him. Well, she wasn't going to be left behind. She would run along the top of the cliff to the place where the path went down to the beach, then cross the sand and swim out to the boats too. She was sure that she could swim as well as he could. But the first thing was to get down to the beach.

When Robert reached the water's edge he knew that the easy part of the plan was behind him. The water, reflecting back the first rays of the rising moon, looked very bright. There was no way that he could swim out to the boats, right in front of the men, without being noticed. His courage wavered; for a moment he considered going back, but when he thought of Kartan waiting in the cave he knew he had to go on.

He clipped his scout knife to his belt and buckled it around his waist. It rubbed against his bare skin. Still hidden by low rocks, he crawled into the water, shivering slightly in anticipation of the first wave washing over him, but the water was surprisingly warm. He pushed out into deeper water, swimming

68

straight out so that he would cross the bay as far as possible from the shore.

He used a breaststroke, making no splash, keeping his head low in the water. Then, thinking he heard a shout from the shore, he cautiously turned his head and looked back over his shoulder. To his horror he saw that the men were no longer grouped around the fire but were standing at the water's edge, all gazing in his direction. He might as well turn back. Then he saw that he was not alone in the water. Coming in from the open sea was a large group of swimmers and that was what the men were watching. As the closest swimmer drew near, Robert found, to his amazement, that he was looking into the round black eyes and comical bewhiskered face of a seal. The seals surrounded him, never coming closer than a few feet, and regarded him with round-eyed stares.

Robert felt no fear of the seals. Many of his grandfather's stories had been about seals—"the selkie folk," he had called them. His grandfather said that seals were really humans banished to the sea for their sins and, if your need was great enough, they would help you and then they could take human form again, leaving their sealskin empty on the shore.

"Selkies! Selkies!" he whispered softly. "I need your help!"

The seals seemed to gather closer around him.

"We'll swim over to the boats together," he told them.

Almost as if they understood, the seals matched their pace to his and swam alongside him right under the gaze of the men on the shore. Gradually the men lost interest and returned to the fireside, looking up only occasionally to watch the progress of the seals. They were not alarmed when they saw them surround the boats. Seals were known for their curiosity.

When Robert reached the boats he thought, for a moment, that the whole long swim had been for nothing. The anchor ropes appeared to be made of twisted strands of metal, too thick for his knife to cut. But, on looking closer, he saw that it *was* rope and only appeared silvery from the drops of water and crust of algae glistening in the moonlight.

Carefully unclipping his knife from his belt—he was terrified that it would slip out of his fingers—he opened the blade and began to saw at the thick rope. Sometimes an inquisitive seal would peer over his shoulder for a minute, and he would talk to it quietly, explaining what he was doing. Then it would dive off, and another would take its place.

Cutting the rope took a long time, but luck was still with Robert because the weight of the boat and the pull of the current were enough to break the rope before he had sawed it entirely through. The boat lurched sideways and began drifting in the direction of the rocks.

Now he had to swim quickly back. If things worked out as he hoped they would, the men would soon be occupied with saving the boat, and Kartan's people would be on their way up the cliff. Robert would have to hurry if he was not going to be left behind.

The seals surrounded him. They let him set the pace, circling and somersaulting around him. The men by the fire still seemed to be watching him, and Robert hoped they would soon pay some attention to their boat.

As Robert neared the shore the seals became uneasy in the shallow water. For a few minutes more they circled around him, almost as if they were begging him to join them, but when he continued shoreward, they drifted back out to sea, abandoning him.

He crawled up the sand and lay still, exhausted by the long swim. His clothes lay beside him in a little heap, like a skin left by a selkie that has taken human form.

A sudden shout drove all thoughts of his grandfather's stories from his mind. Had the men seen him coming out of the water? He snatched up his clothes and began to race up the beach, still crouched behind the rocks. He had almost reached the cliff before he dared look back. To his relief, he saw that the men were scrambling down the rocky shore on the far side of the bay, intent on preventing their boat from being damaged on the rocks.

71

# chapter 6

It took Jennifer far longer than she had anticipated to reach the place where the path went down to the beach. She had intended to follow the contour of the clifftop, but in one place the ground was crumbling away and she had to cut back through the dark wood. She almost gave up rather than penetrate the threatening silence. It had been bad enough during the day, but what sort of night creatures might be lurking there? Her every step was accompanied by the noisy rustling of leaves or the sharp crack of a broken branch alerting the silent forest creatures to the presence of an intruder.

Cautiously she made her way back to the clifftop again and was puzzled to see that Robert had been joined by about a dozen other swimmers. In fact, she could not tell which of the dark heads in the water belonged to him. And the men around the fire seemed to be paying no attention to the swimmers at all.

Assuming that Robert was among the swimmers, he was closer to the boats than she had expected him to be. She wasn't going to catch up. She felt trapped in a nightmare where events happened without connection or consequence, and she struggled to escape from it, but there was no awakening. Ahead, the trees crowded densely to the edge of the cliff, their roots trailing down over the loose soil like grasping fingers, and she realized that in order to continue she would have to go back into the wood. Although the air had cooled with the sun going down, her hair clung damply to the sweat on her forehead and neck, and her legs shook as she inched her way forward between the trees.

Guided by the sound of the sea down below on her right, she finally came to a small clearing on the cliff-top and saw that she had reached the path. Cautiously she edged forward, wondering if she dared climb down in the darkness. It would be almost impossible not to dislodge a few stones and make a lot of noise. Then she noticed that the men were no longer sitting around the fire but were scrambling down the rocks toward one of their boats, which appeared to be drifting toward the rocky shore. Was Robert in the boat? If so, he was going to be caught again. And what had happened to all the other swimmers?

A new sound claimed her attention. The rattle of

stones on the cliff below and the whisper of soft voices. People were climbing the cliff.

The moon was up, giving a fair amount of light in the open, so she drew back into the cover of the trees. Soon a gray-clad figure with long black hair pulled himself up over the edge of the cliff, followed by another, then by several more. They disappeared into the trees only a few yards from her and walked stealthily away. Even in the darkness they walked with great assurance.

Jennifer could not see the people clearly, but they reminded her of Kartan. She wanted to speak to them but didn't quite have the courage. Nevertheless, she edged forward, thinking she might try to follow them and find out where they were going. Anything would be better than being alone again.

She stood behind a tree, hardly concealed at all now, waiting for the next person to come up the cliff. This one, whoever he was, seemed to be having more trouble than the others. Someone was reaching down from the top, giving words of direction or encouragement, and two other people waited at the edge of the trees. Slowly, a tousled head appeared, and with the moon shining directly on his face, Jennifer saw that it was Robert.

"Robert!" she shouted, springing out of the bushes and giving everyone such a fright that Robert was nearly pushed back down the cliff.

"What's wrong?" asked an anxious voice from below.

"Nothing's wrong!" Robert said. "It's Jennifer—she's up here waiting for us. Jennifer!"

"Am I glad to see you!" said Jennifer.

Robert pulled himself the rest of the way up onto the cliff and was immediately surrounded by gray-cloaked people, who all stared at Jennifer.

"I thought you were in the boats!" Jennifer shook her head as if still trying to recover from the surprise of seeing him. "I was sure I saw you running down the sand and then swimming out to the boats."

"Did you see me do that?" Robert's earnest features brightened with a sudden smile. "And did you see the seals? Where were you, anyway?"

"Come," said Kartan, pulling anxiously at Robert's jacket. "There will be time for talk later—at the stone circle."

"Is that where you are going?" Jennifer asked eagerly. "Surely we'll be able to get home from there —away from all this."

It took only a few minutes to reach the clearing in the trees surrounded by the massive standing stones. Once again, Robert puzzled over this.

People sat down in small groups, talking together and sharing mealbread. Kartan offered Robert and Jennifer each a small piece, which they accepted and ate hungrily.

"You know, these stones must have moved," Robert said to Jennifer. "They should be farther from the sea."

"I wish you'd quit going on about that and figure

some way to get us back home," Jennifer answered impatiently.

"I told you that it is the sea that has moved," Kartan said quietly to Robert. "At the time of the Great Floods. It is part of our history."

"The sea couldn't have moved as far as that," Robert protested.

"When the Technological Society was at its greatest height, so many gases and pollutants were produced that the very atmosphere and climate of the earth changed," Kartan said. He was using that singsong voice he had used earlier, almost as if he were reciting from memory. "It is hard for our people to understand, but the climate grew warmer so that the ice caps at the north and south poles melted—we learn all this at the Learning House—and the sea became greater and the land smaller."

"This kind of talk isn't going to get us back home," interrupted Jennifer angrily. "That's what we should be thinking about."

"But don't you see, it does tie in," said Robert. "If the coastline changed, then the stones didn't move nearer the sea."

"All the coastal cities were destroyed in the flood," continued Kartan. "There was much famine and disease, but little written history of that time has survived. The history of our people begins after the flood."

"Where did *they* come from?" asked Robert.

"Our people are from the lands of the south, which

became unbearably hot when the climate changed. They came here by boat, seeking a new home in the cooler Northlands, and finally settled on a small plain by a river, building a new town called Kelso. They named it after an old town near there where they found some artifacts.

"One of the boats sailing to the Northlands was blown off course, and our forefathers thought that these people, too, settled these northern islands. We call that branch of our people the Lost Ones, and hope to meet up with them some year on our summer journey. That is why my first thought was that you were two of the Lost Ones."

Jennifer had meantime moved over into the gap between the stones and was digging down into the soil. Looking up, she shouted to Robert, "Hey! You should be digging too, to get us out of here!"

"We can't go yet," said Robert. "I haven't even had a chance to find out if Duncan is here."

"This has nothing to do with Duncan," answered Jennifer. Then she shrugged and added, "Ask him if you want. Just make it quick 'cause I'm not planning on hanging around."

Robert was conscious of the sharp note in Jennifer's voice, and of the brown people all watching them with slightly puzzled expressions on their smooth faces.

"Has Duncan Guthrie dropped in from our time?" Jennifer asked Kartan with more than a trace of sarcasm.

77

"I only know of Andrew and Elinor, and Ollie and Ian from your time," Kartan answered quietly.

"You mean there *have* been others?" asked Jennifer in surprise, sinking back on her heels and forgetting her digging. "What happened to them?"

"They went back."

"Back? How?"

"There's this old blind woman, called Vianah, who can tell us," Robert broke in eagerly. "I think we should go and see her."

"I'm not moving from these stones," said Jennifer. "I've been thinking about it, and I'm just sure that we have to dig down to the fallen stones again—and you're going to dig, too!"

"Please let's wait," begged Robert.

"And get caught by these Barbaric Ones? Not likely! Now, dig!"

"But there's still so much to find out," protested Robert. "Aren't you curious about all this?"

"All I'm curious about is how to get away from here," answered Jennifer, clawing at the turf.

Robert went over to the next gap and halfheartedly began to pull at the grass and dig into the soil. It was hard-packed and didn't come away as easily as the loose, peaty soil they had dug into before.

Kartan sat beside them, watching uneasily.

Suddenly Savotar's voice rang out into the circle. "The Barbaric Ones are coming again. I hear their voices. We cannot stay here. It will be safer if we flee in small groups and meet again at the Crossing

Place. You, Kartan, take these children with you and travel by the northern route."

Savotar gave hurried instructions to the rest of his people, who quickly slipped into the blackness of the wood. Robert followed Kartan to the edge of the circle and hesitated, not knowing whether to go with Kartan or stay with Jennifer, who was kneeling between the stones, as rigid as if she were carved from rock herself. Then he heard someone crashing through the woods toward them.

"Jennifer, we've got to hide," he pleaded desperately.

Jennifer got stiffly to her feet. "You win," she said. "But this time let's stick together. I don't want to be left alone here again."

# chapter 7

They followed Kartan into the blackness of the wood. All around they could hear leaves rustling and branches snapping, but they could not tell if these sounds were made by the running feet of their own people or of the Barbaric Ones. At last they paused, and now all was still except for their own pounding hearts and rapid breathing.

"We should have got out of here while we had the chance," Jennifer said to Robert.

"Hush!" Kartan cautioned her. "Voices carry in the night air."

They traveled on in silence, but with less urgency now. The forest was denser and the undergrowth thick and tangled, so that Robert wondered how this could be described as the northern route—or any route at all—for there was no path to follow.

"We will rest here," said Kartan, stopping suddenly in a small clearing. Robert and Jennifer were so exhausted that they sank down on the mossy ground and fell asleep almost right away, without any need for blankets or pillows.

They were awakened by a heavy shower of rain, and then the sun came out again, bathing the forest in steamy heat.

Looking at the position of the sun, Kartan said anxiously, "We have slept longer than we should. We must hurry on."

A little farther on they came to a small stream. Kartan followed its course, walking in the clear water. He did not bother to take off the leather thong sandals he wore, and Jennifer and Robert waded into the water with their shoes on, too. Both were wearing socks and sneakers, which squelched rather uncomfortably as they walked, but it was a relief not to have to fight bushes and trees. After some time the stream joined a large river.

"Let us stop here and eat," said Kartan, producing another leaf-wrapped package of mealbread from the pocket of his cloak. "We can drink water from the stream."

They sank down thankfully onto the soft grass, and Robert asked, trying not to sound too anxious, "How much farther do we have to go?"

"It is still a long way," answered Kartan. "But it is easier now that we are following the river. My people use the rivers for travel through the forest—sometimes on foot, and sometimes by raft."

The river was broad and swift, its surface broken into a thousand shining mirrors as the water rippled over stones. The food and freedom from the darkness of the trees revived the spirits of all three.

"Are there wild animals in the wood?" Jennifer asked, looking behind her into the shadows.

"No, there are no animals to fear," answered Kartan. "Are you thinking of the tigers and elephants and dinosaurs of long ago? There are none here— only rabbits, squirrels, foxes, and a few wild dogs. But I have seen pictures in books of the wealth of animals in your time. I would give much to see them for myself."

"You mean there are no tigers or elephants anywhere in the world?"

"They died out in the years of famine and flood. The climate changed suddenly, and they could not adapt."

"You can't know they *all* died out," said Robert. "Maybe some survived in other places. You wouldn't find them here anyway because elephants never did live in Scotland."

"What you say may be true," said Kartan. "Some day I will travel to other lands and find elephants and dinosaurs."

"Not dinosaurs!" interrupted Jennifer. "They're extinct for sure. But I do hope you find elephants."

"I don't see how you know so much about our time when there is so little left," said Robert.

"Tomorrow I shall be able to show you," said Kartan.

They followed the river for many miles. Both Jennifer and Robert were greatly relieved when Kartan said at last that it was time to sleep. They found a little cave formed by the roots of a big tree close to the river and, although it was raining again, they were quite snug.

"This is our second night away," said Jennifer. "Do you think they're looking for us?"

"I've been wondering about that, too," said Robert. "My mum will be in an awful state. They'll think I've run away like Duncan just because I didn't want to go after the sheep."

"You really miss your brother, don't you?" Jennifer asked quietly.

"It was better before he went away," said Robert. "Dad can't do all the farm work on his own. He's always after me to help, and I'm no good at it—not like Duncan was. When the tractor broke down Duncan could fix it himself, and he could make just about anything. The only thing I'm good at is drawing. And that's not much use if you're going to be a farmer."

It was somehow comforting to both of them to talk about home. It strengthened the feeling that their own world was still there, waiting for them to come back. That their parents and friends were still real, even though they were somehow far away. It was this new world that wasn't real.

Soon after, the weariness of their bodies won, and they sank into a dreamless sleep.

It was still dark when Kartan roused them the next morning and said that they must continue their journey. He gave them each a piece of mealbread, which they nibbled silently, crouched in the shelter of the roots.

It seemed the longer they stayed, the more real this new world became to them, and their own life and time a little less real. This morning even Jennifer felt less urgency about getting back, and a little more excitement and interest in what the new day promised.

"Do we have to start while it's still dark?" asked Robert. "We could make just as good time if we waited for daylight."

"You must come with me now," said Kartan urgently. "There is something I want you to see."

Robert and Jennifer crawled out from the shelter of the tree roots. Robert, whose brown coat was old and shabby, looked less untidy than Jennifer did. She scrubbed at a mud stain on her jacket and tried ineffectively to smooth her tangled red hair with her fingers. Kartan was the least rumpled of the three. Wrapped in his gray cloak, he led them down to the river.

The water was cold, but once they had shaken off the heaviness of sleep, it was rather pleasant to be out so early. The silence was broken by a chorus of bird-song, and something of Kartan's suppressed excitement communicated itself to them.

The river was faster now, almost a torrent, and they were being rushed along. It was hard to keep their footing, and they could hear the roar of a waterfall ahead.

"We have to go back into the forest here," said Kartan. "Stay close beside me."

"Can't we wait till it's light?" asked Jennifer, some of her fears of the forest crowding back.

"It is only a little way," said Kartan. "We must go quickly. Nothing delays the rising of the sun."

The trees ended suddenly, and they found themselves standing on a high ledge. They gazed at the scene before them in breathless wonder. To their right the river spilled over the edge of the cliff in a mighty waterfall, plunging into a black pool far below, then snaking around in a great sweep to join the sea. At first all was dim in the shadows and mist, but then it was suddenly bathed in the red-gold light of the rising sun.

However, it was not the unexpected sight of the waterfall nor of the sea that took their breath away. It was the splendor of the works of man. Below them, on a spit of land, bound on one side by the curve of the river and on the other by the sea, rose a huge ruined city. Tall buildings stood intact, although in places the forest and the sands were encroaching. Here and there windows still had glass, and it reflected back the golden glow of the sun so that the buildings appeared lit from within, which gave an illusion of life. The dawn light was kind to the city. It looked as it must have long ago when people lived there, but the noon sun would reveal it as an empty shell, nothing but cracked remains and tumbling ruins.

"What's the name of this place?" asked Jennifer. "I never knew there was a city like this in Scotland."

"It isn't any place I've ever been to, or heard of," said Robert, shaking his head.

"It is the city of Norsea," Kartan told them. "Perhaps it was built after your time. I think it was built in the twenty-first century, shortly before the years of famine and flood."

"There was no city here before that? Nothing in our time?" asked Robert.

"I do not think so," answered Kartan. "Some people became very rich when oil was discovered under the North Sea—oil was greatly valued then—and they built a city that was to withstand all warfare and disasters. They boasted that they were building a city that would last forever, and it *has* outlasted all other towns. But it has outlasted the people, too."

"No one lives there now?" asked Jennifer.

"No one," answered Kartan. "When we first found it, many years ago, some of our people wanted to live here, but we are happier in a town we have built for ourselves. We have learned much from this place, however. There is a library full of books— more books than we can read in a lifetime—and there are other buildings, such as the hospital and the computer center, the purposes of which we cannot really understand."

"Imagine finding a place like this here in Scotland," marveled Jennifer, looking down at the tall, smooth buildings. "In America I might believe it—but a city like this in Scotland!"

"I don't see why it shouldn't be in Scotland," said Robert loyally, although he understood what Jennifer meant. It was too planned and all of a piece. The towns he knew had grown up over centuries and the main streets weren't wide enough for cars.

"It's such a relief to find something in this place besides endless forest," said Jennifer. "Can we go down and see it?"

"Yes," answered Kartan. "There will be much that you can explain."

Rough steps had been cut into the cliff, and they descended easily to the city. Robert and Jennifer could not shake off the feeling that they were trespassers as they walked past the tall buildings, and they spoke only in whispers.

"We can go inside," said Kartan and he led them through a high, vaulted arch into some sort of office building. Robert and Jennifer were a little disappointed by it. The carpeting and furniture had all mildewed and rotted and been devoured by insects in the damp, warm climate, but the metal cabinets and machines were still stark and intact. The building would have been more interesting if the escalators and computer systems had worked, but when the last electric generator failed the whole building had died, locking all its secrets behind great metal panels with a few knobs and switches. As if to symbolize this, there was a robot standing by the doorway, as lifeless as the building.

"I bet you asked him questions and he answered them when all this was operating," said Jennifer, greatly intrigued by the idea. "He would be a kind of mechanical doorman."

For the first time since the adventure started, she had lost her preoccupation with where she was and how to get back and was interested in what she was seeing.

"Can you direct me to Mr. Smith's office?" she asked the robot with a mock curtsy.

"First door on the left," said a hollow voice.

Jennifer's mouth fell open, then Robert stepped from behind the robot, laughing.

"That wasn't fair!" said Jennifer, but she laughed, too.

Next Kartan took them to the library. He told them that it was his people's favorite part of the city and that they had taken many books back to their own town of Kelso to study them.

There was no library in Locharden, but Robert had been to the one in Baldry. He had been greatly impressed by the number of books—the room had even smelled of books. But that was nothing compared to the number of books here. The building was tall and narrow, and Robert felt as if he were enclosed in a tower whose walls were built of books. Metal bookcases soared above him, and metal staircases connected galleries and walkways at different levels.

Jennifer, perhaps because she had been in big libraries before, was less awed than Robert and wandered about taking books off the shelves and replacing them. She pulled open a wide drawer in a metal cabinet that stood in the middle of the room.

"Hey! Look at this! I've found some newspapers and the news is all about stuff in the future."

"Does it tell what happened to everyone?" Robert asked in a timid voice.

"It's not that kind of news," said Jennifer cheerfully. "Listen to this! 'Billy Johnson, aged eighteen months, won a medal for first place in the Norsea Bouncing Baby Contest on Saturday. He swallowed the medal and had to be rushed to the hospital. Both medal and baby survived the ordeal!'"

"There must be something more important than that," said Robert in a pained voice.

"How about football scores? The Rangers beat the Celtics last Saturday," said Jennifer brightly.

Rangers and Celtics belonged comfortably to Robert's own life, and he was interested immediately.

"What's the date of that paper?" he asked excitedly. "We could find the football results for some Saturday next winter and win a fortune in the pools!"

"It's March 15, 2010! Do you want to wait till you're over forty to make your fortune?"

"I can't wait that long," said Robert. "Find something closer to our own time."

"I can't find anything here," said Jennifer, rifling through the pile.

"What is it you want to know?" Kartan asked. He had listened to their conversation with a puzzled expression. "There is much that we cannot comprehend in the books and papers here."

"We want some earlier newspapers," said Jennifer, pulling out another drawer.

It contained maps and atlases, which Kartan said were useless to his people because the maps were of the way the land looked before the floods. "But you can show me where you live," he said, lifting the atlas from the drawer.

They crouched around it, flipping over the pages until they found a map of Scotland. Locharden was too small to be marked on it.

"I will show you where Savotar thinks our people journeyed from," Kartan said, turning to a map of India. "We cannot be completely sure, because much history was lost at the time of the floods, but we believe that our people came from a valley in these mountains, north of India."

"How come you speak English and not Hindustani or something?" asked Jennifer.

"I think our people spoke English even in our homeland," said Kartan slowly. "Then when we came to the Northlands, a few people were here already and they spoke English. But ask Savotar—he knows more of our history than I do."

"What happened to the people who were already here?" asked Robert.

"They joined us. We are always eager for more people to join us. We need many people to keep our society viable."

"We have the opposite problem in our time," said Robert. "Too many people—especially in places like India."

Jennifer went back to resume her search for a newspaper, but Robert wanted to go and see another building. He had the uncomfortable feeling that he wasn't making the most of his opportunity to understand the future, but at the same time he realized that it might be a burden to know too much.

Kartan wanted them to see the hospital. The size and complexity of the place greatly impressed his people, he told them.

"There was so much sickness and so many plagues in your time," Kartan said, shaking his head as he looked at a long ward of rusting hospital beds. "They say that those who were ill were kept apart from other people in this hospital."

"You're wrong about plagues," said Jennifer. "That was earlier than our time."

"What do you do when you get sick?" asked Robert.

"We do not get sick," answered Kartan. "Savotar

says that there was more stress in your day and that people did not eat well."

"You're thinking about the famine and the floods that came after us."

"Savotar says there was illness long before the flood, caused by poor food and worry. He has spoken of cancer and heart illness and chicken pox."

"I've had chicken pox," said Jennifer. "It isn't so bad, except I had it on my birthday and I couldn't have a party. But it was caused by germs or a virus—not by worry."

"Perhaps when animals like elephants died out, germs died out too," suggested Kartan. "I never heard of our people being sick with chicken pox."

They had wandered outside again, for there was not really much to see in the hospital, and were now standing in front of a church. It was an impressive building with a tower at one end, and made Robert think of a huge ship cresting the waves. Some of the stained-glass windows were still unbroken so that when they stepped inside they were bathed in purple and gold light. The roof seemed to float above the walls, and a huge sculpture dominated the front of the church.

Kartan was satisfied by their awe, for he, too, greatly loved this building. On the whole his people did not admire the people of the Technological Age, but the first time he had seen this church he had begun to believe that there were things that technology had produced that would never be duplicated.

"It's like a painting," said Robert softly, looking up at the sweep of the walls and the roof.

"What do you mean?" asked Jennifer.

"I know," said Kartan quietly. "It gives me that feeling, too."

Robert looked at him and a wave of understanding passed between them.

"There is a bell tower that we can climb and look out over the whole city," Kartan said, leading them to a small door at the far end of the building. He unbolted it and they ran up a long flight of winding stone stairs until they emerged on a little platform below the bell.

Something bright, caught in a deep crack between two floor tiles, caught Jennifer's eye. Working carefully, she managed to loosen a thin chain. Pulling it out of the crack, she found a large, plain cross attached to the chain.

"That looks like gold," said Robert, taking it from her and examining it. "It could be worth a fortune."

"You may keep it if you like it," said Kartan casually.

"It's not yours to give away," Robert pointed out. "And if it really is gold, it's worth a great deal of money."

"It is worth nothing now," said Kartan with a shrug. "Take it if you value it."

Jennifer put it around her neck and looked doubtfully from Kartan to Robert.

"You can't keep it!" said Robert sternly.

"Well, I'm not just going to shove it down the crack again," said Jennifer. "Nobody else wants it. Besides, *they* take things from here all the time. You heard Kartan say they take books from the library."

"But that's gold," said Robert, still troubled.

Kartan tried to interest them in the view from the tower, but they were too concerned with the chain to give the view more than a casual glance. Otherwise, they might have seen a heavy figure crossing the square below. Kartan led them back down the stairs, and when they reached the bottom, they stopped short, wide-eyed with terror, for there, filling the small doorway, was one of the Barbaric Ones. The same bearded giant who had chased them through the woods two days before.

They were trapped.

The man was, for one moment, almost as surprised as they were. Then he said something in his harsh, guttural tongue, stepped back outside the door, and slammed it shut. They heard the ominous sound of the bolt sliding into its socket.

# chapter 8

Jennifer, Robert, and Kartan huddled together in the small room, listening to the dying echo of the man's footsteps as he walked away through the church.

"Why did he lock us in here?" Jennifer whispered. "What's he going to do next?"

"I do not know," said Kartan. His face was white in the dim light, his eyes enormous. "Maybe he is going to leave us here until he is ready to travel north again, or maybe he has gone to tell his companions."

Robert rattled the door, although he knew it was useless.

"We should have stayed at the stone circle," said Jennifer angrily. "We might as well have been caught there as trapped here. At least while we were there, there was a chance of getting home. And *you* don't even care."

"I do," protested Robert. "It was just that I thought if we could reach Vianah—"

"Vianah!" said Jennifer scornfully. "You pin all your hopes on someone you've never seen."

As always happened when Jennifer and Robert disagreed, Kartan looked disturbed and perplexed. His look made Jennifer aware of the sharpness of her voice but, instead of calming her, this made her angrier than ever.

"You got us into this mess by getting caught in the first place," she said spitefully to Robert. "We could have stayed in the woods near the circle and then gone home without getting involved."

"But I saved Savotar and the others by swimming out to the boats. I helped them get away from the cave."

"What's the good of that now that we're caught again?"

"*They're* still free," said Robert.

"And we end up being martyrs for a cause that is still two hundred years in the future," said Jennifer sarcastically.

"There *is* a way out of here—across the roof," Kartan interrupted quietly. "Aetherix and I once got out that way when we were playing here with the others."

"Then why are we just standing here?" Jennifer asked.

"It is not easy," Kartan warned them. "And the Barbaric Ones may see us."

"Anything would be better than waiting," said Robert.

They followed Kartan back up the stairs, and this time they were more interested in the view. The bell tower rose above the church by a height of about ten feet. They scanned the city below them, but nothing moved.

"Do you see him anywhere?" Kartan asked.

Robert shook his head. "But maybe he can see us."

"We shall take that chance," said Kartan. "We are going to drop down onto the roof below and cross it. There is a way down the far side that is not difficult."

Robert looked down at the sheer drop to the sloping roof of the main building, shuddered, and closed his eyes. It was all right for the others, who had legs they could depend on, to drop onto that steep roof, but he knew he couldn't do it.

Jennifer, who had been watching him, said quietly, "I'm sorry about what I said down there. I always get mad when I'm scared. You should hear the way I go on at home when I'm worried about a test or something. Mom says—"

"I can't make it," said Robert flatly. "You go ahead with Kartan."

"We were going to stick together this time—remember?"

Kartan had climbed to a narrow ledge between two pillars that supported the roof of the bell tower. He lowered himself over the other side and dropped lightly onto the curved roof of the church below.

"You're next," Jennifer said to Robert.

He stood there, biting his lip, looking down at Kartan, who was beckoning to them anxiously.

"You go," he said to Jennifer.

"No! Not unless you do!"

He might never have jumped except that sounds from the stairwell filled him with an even greater fear. A door banged. Footsteps sounded on the stairs. Jennifer helped him up onto the wall where he clung for only a second and then let go, slithering down the wall, scraping his knees and landing sprawling beside Kartan. Jennifer almost landed on top of them.

"Come on," said Kartan, dragging Robert by his sleeve. They crawled across the roof and swung down to a lower roof above the entryway to the church. From there they jumped to the ground. Robert was aching all over and so shaken that all he wanted to do was rest, but there was no chance of that. They were once again involved in a frightful game of hide-and-seek, this time among the ghostly buildings of the deserted city. A shout from the tower warned them that they had been spotted as they ran across the open space between the church and the library. Ducking inside the building, they came face to face with another bearded man, who was so taken aback by their sudden appearance that he did not immediately give chase.

From the library they ran down a broad street and finally took refuge in a small house overlooking the sea. It was the first Norsea house that Jennifer and

Robert had been inside, and if they had not been in such a state of panic, they would have found it interesting. Even so, Jennifer did explore a little. The living room seemed to have a sunken conversation area, all the furniture being built into the room, and in the middle of the house there was either a lily pond or a bath tub—she never decided which—and the kitchen looked like a laboratory. Afterward she remarked to Robert that it might have been a laboratory that looked like a kitchen. Robert slumped against a wall and stared out a glassless window, while Kartan prowled nervously around.

"Is that the sea or the river?" Robert asked Kartan when he finally recovered enough to take in his surroundings. "There's land on the other side."

"It is an arm of the sea. It separates our island from the Far Northland. In your time this was all one land, but when the water rose the land was divided into many islands."

"And Kelso lies across the water?"

Kartan nodded.

"How do we get there?"

"Do you see that spit of land below us? When the tide is out, as it is now, most of the sand is uncovered. We can wade across."

"Then this is the Crossing Place that Savotar talked about?" asked Jennifer, joining them again.

"Yes," said Kartan. "I fear that Savotar and the others will be here soon, and will be caught by these men. That is probably what they are hoping for."

"They're walking into a trap," said Robert.

Kartan stood staring out at the water, his fingers drumming on the windowsill. He turned to Robert, his face taut and strained.

"You saved my people earlier by swimming out to the boat. Maybe *I* can do something now, but I shall have to ask you to accept a great risk."

"The risk of being caught by the Barbaric Ones?" Jennifer asked nervously.

"The risk of drowning," said Kartan, his eyes moving anxiously from one to the other.

"You should be all right!" Jennifer said encouragingly to Robert.

"I have never made the crossing alone," Kartan continued. "But I think I know the secret of it—the tree and the rock must be kept in line. Aetherix and I planned to cross by ourselves someday to see if we were right." He paused, staring out again across the stretch of water. "If I am wrong, then we might easily step into the sinking sands and be trapped by the rising tide."

"That wouldn't be any worse than being caught by these Barbaric Ones," said Jennifer with a shudder.

"And you, Robert?"

"I'll come."

"Then it is time to go. We shall go straight down from here to the beach across the salt marsh where the white cotton rushes are blooming. When we reach the water you must follow close behind me, stepping only where I step. There is soft sand on either side, and the currents are treacherous here where the Ocean of the East meets the Ocean of the West. *And do not look back!*"

Kartan jumped lightly through the empty window frame and ran down toward the beach making no attempt to keep hidden. From somewhere behind them they heard shouting voices. They had been seen by the Barbaric Ones.

They could easily have crept down behind a low wall that ran some distance toward the sea, Robert thought angrily to himself, instead of practically inviting the Barbaric Ones to follow them. What was the point of escaping from Norsea, only to be trapped in the woods on the other side of the water? Robert knew that he could not run much farther.

They had reached the water's edge. Although he did not know these waters, Robert could see that the tide had turned and was racing quickly up the beach, lifting dry particles of sand and bits of seaweed which formed a scum on the advancing wave.

"We've got to be quick," said Kartan, his voice hoarse and anxious. "Stay close behind me, stepping only where I step. And remember, do not look back!"

Robert clung to Kartan's words as to a talisman and followed him confidently into the water, which soon reached his knees, his thighs. He tried to shut out the excited sound of the voices of the pursuing men as they walked steadily forward. He could feel the sand shifting under his feet and the pull of the current as the water eddied past. Now the water was deeper, and

Kartan hesitated ahead of him as if probing the sand with his feet. After a moment of doubt, he again pressed confidently forward.

They were almost waist deep in the water. The current was stronger now, dragging the sand from under their feet. Jennifer, who was holding the back of Robert's jacket, gave a strangled cry; but Robert did not turn around.

Gradually the feel of the sand under their feet changed and became firm. The water was shallower again, and Kartan broke into a splashy run. Robert stumbled and crawled the last few feet to the beach, lying there for a minute fighting for his breath. He could hear the shouts of the Barbaric Ones, urgent, close, but he scarcely had the energy to care. Finally he turned around, and at the sight of the men in the water, he dragged himself to his feet.

The men were shouting, and their cries were not of anger or triumph, but of fear. They had plunged into the water after the three children, unaware of the narrow line that separated safety from disaster in those foreign waters. They were caught in the sinking sands. The more they struggled to be free, the more firmly embedded their feet became in the treacherous footing.

The tidewater was racing in, and five of the six men were hopelessly caught. The only one who managed to free himself was being swept away by the racing tide and carried farther and farther to the east. Robert thought it was the bearded one who had chased them twice, but the man was too far away for him to be sure.

Kartan was standing on dry sand, his face twisted with pain as he watched the struggling men. He ran to the water's edge and shouted to them, "Line up the tree and the white stone! The tree and the stone! Move to the west!" But the men could not understand his words, and anyway, they came too late.

"I see now what Savotar means when he says we cannot respond to violence with violence," said Kartan brokenly. "I shall know no peace now."

"It wasn't your fault," said Jennifer stoutly. "They didn't *have* to follow."

But all of them knew that Kartan had acted against the faith of his people while trying to save them.

Robert was too weary to think of anything comforting to say. Kartan, glad of something physical to do, began to weave a shelter for them out of the branches of a willow.

When it was finished, Robert curled up on a bed of leaves and moss and fell into a dreamless sleep. The next morning, stiff and sore but considerably refreshed, he was able to continue the journey with the others.

# chapter 9

In the morning they followed a well-marked trail through the forest, the ground spongy under their feet, for it had rained heavily in the night. Droplets of water glistened on the foliage all around them.

Kartan walked in silence, still apparently worrying about what had happened to the Barbaric Ones at the Crossing Place the day before. Finally, in response to a question from Robert, he answered, "We will soon be in Kelso. I hope that Panchros and Alloperla are already there—that they are safe from the Barbaric Ones."

"Are they your father and mother?" Jennifer asked.

"They are my Chosen Ones," answered Kartan.

"Meaning?"

"In our ninth year we take part in the Ceremony of the Choosing. That is when we decide on our Chosen Ones, who then become to us rather like a mother or father, but also like a teacher. We no longer go to the Learning House, but learn from them."

"Do you choose brothers and sisters, too?" Robert asked. "You spoke of Aetherix as your Chosen Brother."

"I chose Panchros and Alloperla as Chosen Ones because they are great artists and I love to draw. Aetherix—he was thirteen—had already chosen them four years before, so we became Chosen Brothers."

"And before you were nine? Who looked after you then?"

"The youngest children, from the time they are born until they are three or four years old, live together in the Baby House."

"Do their mothers and fathers live there, too?" Jennifer asked.

Kartan shook his head. "People who choose to be with the babies live there, and others come in to help. I often go over to the Baby House to play with the little ones."

"But where are the mothers and fathers these babies belong to?"

"The babies belong to all of us," answered Kartan, looking puzzled.

"But don't the mothers *want* to keep their babies themselves?"

"Many new mothers work in the Baby House, but a baby is not something someone owns. A new baby is a gift for all of us."

Jennifer wasn't sure she approved of that philosophy. After a few minutes of silence, she asked, "After they leave the Baby House, what then?"

"They are old enough to live in the town, staying in each house in turn for a few weeks or months. They learn to read and write, to sing, to sew and paint in the Learning House. They work in the gardens, the drying kilns, the laundry, and the fish canal."

"The fish canal—what's that?"

"Down by the river we have dug canals where we raise fish. It is easier to catch them there in the still water. The small children enjoy netting them in the shallows—that was my favorite task."

"You don't fish now?" asked Jennifer.

"Sometimes," answered Kartan. "But I prefer to spend my time studying painting with my Chosen Ones. There is much to learn."

"Well, it sounds like real Children's Lib," Jennifer said. "Choosing your own parents! Though I still think I would choose my mom and dad. How about you, Robert?"

Robert hesitated, thinking of all the times he and his father had quarreled over the farm work left undone or about Robert's interest in painting. Even his mother didn't really understand that he *had* to draw things. If only he could have been allowed to choose— but that seemed a terribly disloyal way to think, especially when he was here, not knowing how to get back to them.

"Do children sometimes choose their own parents

as Chosen Ones?" Robert asked, avoiding Jennifer's question.

"I suppose they do," answered Kartan slowly, almost as if he hadn't thought about this before. "But it wouldn't really make any difference. You see, it is—well—more important with us to share than to own."

"Do the Chosen Ones get paid for looking after these kids?" Jennifer asked.

"Paid?" asked Kartan, looking puzzled.

"Yes, paid."

"You mean with money? Like in your time? We have no money in our society," Kartan said.

"The whole thing just doesn't sound workable to me!" said Jennifer, shaking her head.

"You will soon be able to judge for yourself," said Kartan, smiling. "We are almost there."

A few minutes later they stepped out of the forest into a wide clearing beside the river.

Although Kartan had said nothing to indicate that Kelso would resemble Norsea and had, in fact, told them many times that the Age of Technology was completely gone, they had both somehow expected that Kelso would be big and impressive—shining towers and structures of stone rising above the forest as if to show man's supremacy over nature. Instead, Kelso was no more than a group of small houses, scarcely more elaborate than the cottage Robert's grandfather had lived in, clustered on a narrow plain close to the river. Surrounding the houses were some fields and gardens, and behind them were fruit trees, which merged with the trees of the forest. The forest seemed ever-present, pressing close around the houses.

Almost at once Robert was conscious of an aura of peace surrounding the little settlement. The Barbaric Ones had certainly not found the town. Men, women, and children were working in the gardens; people were sitting in their doorways in the sunshine; babies were playing in the dirt.

"First we will go and see Panchros and Alloperla and make sure they have returned safely from their journey," Kartan said, leading them out into the open.

People from all sides ran up to Kartan, greeting him warmly with excited shouts and hugs, but they only smiled shyly at the two strangers. Robert was very aware of how untidy he and Jennifer looked as they stood there among all these smooth-haired people, most of whom wore gray tunics like Kartan's, bright with embroidery. Robert's and Jennifer's clothes seemed all wrong—bulky and rumpled and stained. Robert could tell that Jennifer felt the same way, for her hands flew to her head in a vain effort to smooth her tangled hair.

"My Chosen Ones live on the other side of the town, close to the peach orchard," Kartan said, leading the way.

Jennifer and Robert soon collected a following of small children, frankly curious and perhaps even a little fearful of the two strangers. These were the first people the children had seen who did not live in their own community.

A girl, a little taller than the other children, detached herself from the crowd and came up to Jennifer. Slipping her hand into Jennifer's, she smiled and said, "I like the color of your hair!"

Jennifer smiled back. This was the same remark Scottish children had made when she was new at Locharden School and they had wanted to be friendly. Here, there was more reason to comment on the color of Jennifer's hair because all the children had straight black hair.

"It's a mess," said Jennifer. "I like the embroidery on your shirt."

"It is not well done," said the girl blushing. "I did it myself."

When Jennifer looked closely at this shirt she saw that the stitches were uneven and in places threads hung loose, but the effect was very colorful.

"I couldn't do anything near as good," she said. "When I sew everything gets tangled—or else the thread breaks and then I can't get my needle threaded again."

"I have these troubles, too!" smiled the girl.

"I'm Jennifer. What's your name?"

"Lara Avara."

"Lara Avara! That's pretty. Kartan talked about you."

By now they could see the home of Panchros and Alloperla. It was a small stone house thatched with leaves and shaded by the branches of a peach tree, bent low under the weight of golden fruit. The door and window frames were intricately carved with twisted vines, and the door was painted blue.

"It's like a picture in a fairy tale," Jennifer whispered.

"Alloperla! Panchros! I'm home!" shouted Kartan, running into the house. Jennifer, Robert, and Lara Avara followed him, but the small children swarmed over to the peach tree, helping themselves to the fruit. Kartan's words echoed in Jennifer's and Robert's minds as the sound of children running in from school, back in their own time: "Mother! Dad! I'm home!"

Alloperla was sitting at an easel painting. She was darker skinned than the other brown people, tall, thin and angular, with her black hair swept up onto her head in a style that emphasized her long neck. When she heard Kartan's voice, she threw down her brushes and came running over and hugged him.

"Kartan! Kartan! You are safe!" she said joyfully, and there were tears in her eyes. "How I have worried about you—but here you are! Safe!" And she stood, holding him at arm's length, smiling down at him as if she could not quite believe that he had really returned.

Robert looked around the room and felt that he was in the center of a kaleidoscope. Every inch of the wall was hung with paintings, and more were stacked alongside tables and chairs. Even Alloperla seemed to belong to the hodgepodge of color because, although she was wearing the customary gray clothes that everyone seemed to wear, they were so spattered with paint that they had taken on an individuality.

"Who are these children, Kartan?" she asked, finally able to take her eyes off Kartan himself.

"Robert and Jennifer," Kartan answered. "I have brought them here to see Vianah. I met them at the Circle of Time."

"They are not children of the Barbaric Ones?" Alloperla asked, a little anxiously.

"Of course not!" said Kartan. "I would not have brought them here if they were. They are like Ollie and Ian, the children Vianah talks about."

"The children of another time!" said Alloperla, studying them curiously. "How I would like to paint them!"

"You must not worry!" said Kartan, turning to Robert and Jennifer with a smile. "Alloperla is always painting people. Come and look!"

The canvas that Alloperla was working on was turned so that they could not see it, and when Kartan invited them to look at the painting, Alloperla made a slight motion as if to stop them. Then she shrugged and turned the easel around herself. All the time she watched Kartan anxiously.

It was completely different from the other paintings in the room—stark and fierce—and the effect was all the more horrifying because of Alloperla's gentle quietness. It was a crude painting of wild-eyed men with raised sticks, striking down a small, frightened boy. His white, starfish hands were held above his head to ward off the blows.

"Is it—Aetherix?" Robert asked.

Alloperla nodded.

"Why did you have to paint him that way?" Kartan sobbed. "It makes it all so—so real."

"It is real," said Alloperla roughly. "We cannot always run and hide from the Barbaric Ones and all that they stand for. The evil and cruelty will change us anyway, even if we do nothing against them."

"Do you mean that we should drive them away? Fight them, like Aetherix did?"

"No, Kartan," Alloperla answered sharply. "What Aetherix did was wrong, too. You have read enough history to know that violence must not be matched by violence. No problem was ever solved that way."

"Suppose—suppose they were in trouble and you did not save them. Is that violence, too?" Kartan asked the question almost as if the words were being dragged out of him.

"What sort of trouble do you mean?" Alloperla asked, sensing that this was no idle question.

Kartan sank down into a chair beside the easel and stared at the painting for a long time. Then, speaking in a low voice, he told Alloperla how the Barbaric Ones had followed them over the Crossing and been trapped by the rising tide.

"You knew that they would follow you?" said

Alloperla accusingly. "You guessed what would happen."

Kartan nodded miserably. "I wanted to make it safe for Savotar and the others when they reached Norsea—and for you here in Kelso. There seemed to be no other way."

"It is just as I said," Alloperla answered bitterly. "Their evil ways are already changing us. But we must not let that happen! We must prove that the forces we believe in—love, trust and sharing—are stronger than their lack of trust and greed. But who am I to tell you this? Since Aetherix died, my heart is cold. You must speak with Savotar."

To both Robert and Jennifer this conversation seemed uncomfortably personal, and they pretended not to listen, staring at the paintings on the wall. But Lara Avara crept close to Alloperla, taking one hand in hers, as if trying to comfort her.

The painting in front of Robert was quite small, a picture of gray vertical shapes, seen through a swirling mist. He stared at it for some time before noticing the faint outline of two kneeling figures, in the distance between the gray shapes. He drew in a sharp breath, stepping back from the picture to see it better, and recognized the place at once—the Stones of Arden, draped in mist, with the moor stretching back to the slopes of the mountain.

"Who painted this?" he burst out, forgetting that the others were absorbed in their own discussion.

"Kartan did it last year, when we were on our summer journey," Alloperla answered.

"Kartan! But did you really see it like this—with the moor instead of those dark trees?"

"Only in my mind," answered Kartan. "If you like it, you may have it." Casually, he took the painting from the wall and handed it to Robert, who gazed at it, remembering his own crude attempts to draw the circle of stones. If only he could learn to put on paper the pictures in his mind.

"You must allow me to paint a picture of you to hang in its place," Alloperla was saying, smiling down at him. "Now that Kartan is here, I shall put away the painting of Aetherix. Would you mind staying while I paint you?"

"I don't mind at all," said Robert eagerly. He wanted nothing more than to stay where he was, surrounded by these strange, wonderful pictures. Here, surely, was someone who could teach him to paint the way he wanted to paint.

"I must return to Vianah," Lara Avara said quietly. "Shall I take Jennifer with me?"

"That would be a good idea," said Alloperla. "And you, Kartan, must greet Panchros."

"Where is he?"

"He is in the Cooking House, making supper. By now I am sure he will have had news of your home-coming, and they will be planning a feast tonight in honor of your safe return, and for our guests."

"But why is he in the Cooking House?" Kartan

asked in a puzzled voice. "I have never known him to be interested in cooking."

"He has not lifted a brush since we came back. Perhaps now that *you* are here—The Barbaric Ones are changing us. Without even being here they are taking away our strengths and talents. . . ." Her voice trailed away.

"But cooking—"

"There is art in cooking, too. Tonight you will see that Panchros has that gift."

Kartan and Lara Avara crossed over to the door, but Jennifer hesitated, not wanting to go to Vianah without Robert.

"Why don't you come with us, Robert?" she asked.

"I can't come now," Robert said impatiently. "Alloperla is going to do a painting of me."

"But it's to see Vianah! There's so much to ask her. Don't you want to ask her about those other children who were here? Maybe she'll even know something about Duncan. And about getting home."

"I like it here," said Robert. "I want to stay."

Robert spoke with such feeling that Jennifer was a little frightened. Suppose he didn't mean just for now, but for always?

# chapter 10

"Would you like to see our gardens on the way there?" Lara Avara asked Jennifer.

"O.K." Jennifer answered without much enthusiasm. She wasn't really interested in gardens, but she wasn't eager to meet Vianah yet, either—not without Robert.

Since coming to Scotland she had noticed that whenever they visited people, they were invited to walk around their gardens, learning the history of every shrub. Jennifer, scarcely knowing a pansy from a petunia, found it boring, but this time she couldn't help being impressed. The plants were so leafy and luxurious she felt that if she just stood still for a little, they would grow right up around her. Rows of large, tight cabbages marched between tomato plants laden with ripe red and yellow tomatoes, and vines of cucumber and runner beans tangled with everything.

"I didn't know tomatoes grew outside in Scotland," Jennifer said. "Cabbages, yes! They have this awful boiled cabbage for school dinners. But I thought it was too cold for tomatoes."

"It is always warm here, and the vegetables grow fast during the long days in summer."

Jennifer had been aware of the warmth, especially since she had been wearing her jacket most of the time, but it was only here in the garden that she realized how much the climate had changed the land.

"All these forests," she said thoughtfully. "I bet that when the weather grew warmer new kinds of plants and trees took over. It's the kind of thing we learn in school, but I never thought much about."

But for Lara Avara, the forest had always been there, and she was anxious to show Jennifer the young goats and lambs, so she hurried her on. Then they went to the Baby House.

Jennifer's first impression of the Baby House was of color. The low log building was surrounded by a fenced-in porch. Vines and flowers scrambled over the fence and cascaded from windowboxes, and the doors and window frames were bright orange. Then she noticed the sounds. Someone was singing in a high voice, slightly off key, and children were laughing and clapping. Running feet echoed on the wooden floor, and a little dark-eyed boy appeared at an open window.

"Here's Lara Avara," he shouted. "And she's bringing us a Lost One!"

117

Immediately, dark-eyed, dark-haired toddlers and children filled the doorway, tumbling over each other in their eagerness to see Jennifer.

"They think you are a Lost One!" laughed Lara Avara. "Many of our tales and legends tell about the Lost Ones who will someday return. A favorite with these little ones is the story of the Lost Girl who has hair as red as the sunset and tangled like the branches of briar!"

A chubby little boy held out his arms to Jennifer, and she forgot her embarrassment as she hugged him.

"That's Nephi," said Lara Avara. "He is a favorite with everyone."

Nephi led Jennifer into an inner room where a young man was carving wooden animals for the children to play with. After watching him for a little, they joined the group singing and clapping. Next, Nephi wanted to play with a ball. In his eagerness to catch it, he and a small girl bumped heads, and both of them began to cry loudly. Jennifer comforted them, rocking them in a swinging chair. When Lara Avara suggested they should leave, Nephi cried again, but he brightened up when Jennifer promised that she would come back soon.

Vianah's house lay beyond the fish canal and the drying kiln. It was surrounded by a garden blooming with roses and many flowering plants and shrubs that were new to Jennifer.

"Mmmm! What a pretty garden! It smells so good!"

"Because Vianah cannot see, she knows flowers by their smell," Lara Avara explained. "She knows the names of all the flowers in her garden, and I often take her into the woods to look for new flowers she will enjoy."

"Do you often visit Vianah?" Jennifer asked.

"I live with her. She is my Chosen One—and also Nemourah."

"But they are both women! Don't you have to choose a man and a woman?" Jennifer asked in surprise, for she still thought of Chosen Ones as replacing a mother and father.

"There cannot be rules deciding whom you love and from whom you learn," Lara Avara answered simply.

"But what can you learn from Vianah?" Jennifer asked. "Kartan said she was too old to go on your summer journeys, and she's blind."

"You will understand when you meet her. Being old, she understands more than the rest of us."

Lara Avara pushed open the door of the small cottage, and Jennifer saw a small, wrinkled woman sitting in a rocking chair by the open window. A slight breeze ruffled her wispy white hair. Jennifer hung back shyly.

The old woman looked at her directly, with clear blue eyes, and asked, "Who is this that you have brought to me?"

Jennifer's first thought was that Vianah did not look blind. She was also the first person Jennifer had seen in Kelso who did not have dark brown eyes and black hair.

"Let her touch you," Lara Avara said quietly to Jennifer, then she skipped forward and kissed Vianah's wrinkled cheek, saying, "I have brought you a great surprise. This is Jennifer, another child like Ollie and Ian."

"Come closer, Jennifer!" the old woman said, her voice trembling with excitement.

Feeling dreadfully self-conscious, Jennifer knelt down beside the old woman's chair. Vianah reached out and her cool, dry fingers caressed Jennifer's face and hair. At her touch Jennifer lost her sense of awkwardness, feeling only the old woman's love for her.

"So you are also a child from that other time?"

Jennifer nodded, then remembering that Vianah was blind, said aloud, "We don't know these others who came. We don't even know how we got here."

"You are not alone?"

"My friend Robert is here, too. He is at Alloperla's house."

"Ah, yes! She will want to paint you both! You must bring him here soon. But tell me how you found this place."

Sitting at Vianah's feet, Jennifer recounted the whole story of the stones on the moor, the mists, their escape from the Barbaric Ones, and the journey to Kelso.

"There's so much about all this I can't explain,"

Jennifer concluded. "There's so much that just doesn't make sense."

"Do not be distressed," said Vianah gently. "An active mind is full of questions, for then you have much to think about. It is a dull mind that has only answers!"

Before Jennifer could raise the question she had really come to ask, a bell rang, and Lara Avara said, "It is time for the feast! Are you coming with us, Vianah, or shall I bring your food here?"

"Tonight I will come with you," said Vianah.

"Vianah! It has been a long time since you joined us for a Feast Day!" said Lara Avara, joyfully jumping up to fetch a carved cane and a shawl for Vianah's frail shoulders.

"This is a special Feast Day," said Vianah, patting Jennifer lightly on the cheek.

Jennifer helped Lara Avara lead Vianah to the Cooking House where the feast was to be held. On their way, Jennifer asked Lara Avara about Feast Days.

"On Feast Days everyone eats together down at the Cooking House. When there is nothing special to honor with a feast, someone from each household goes down to the Cooking House and takes home enough food for their people. You would be surprised to know how many things we find to celebrate, for eating together is fun!"

Jennifer had been picturing great plates of meal-bread, but when they arrived at the Cooking House her eyes widened at the sight of a table spread with platters containing many kinds of vegetables, both raw and cooked. Beside them were relishes, sauces, cheese, nuts, and smoked fish. Everything looked and smelled so beautiful that it brought back Alloperla's words that there was art in cooking.

The plates were of fine pottery, each with a different pattern, but all blending the same subtle colors. Jennifer watched nervously as two small children reached for the precious plates and filled them with food.

A short man with a square face and intense, dark eyes was replenishing the platters as they were emptied, and Jennifer guessed that he must be Panchros because Kartan was helping him.

Then she saw Robert near the table, gazing wide-eyed at the variety of foods. Joining him, she said, "It's like those pictures of fancy buffet suppers in Mom's magazines. She's always trying to copy them, but it never works out like the picture."

Robert, whose mother rarely served anything more elaborate than stew and potatoes, said nothing, but he was so hungry that he soon filled his plate. Jennifer took him outside to meet Vianah, who was sitting in the shade, waiting for Lara Avara. Then Lara Avara appeared, followed by Kartan and little Nephi, who plumped himself down beside Jennifer, grinning up at her.

"You'll have to feed him," said Lara Avara. "You are his Chosen One today!"

"What will I give him?"

"Let him decide."

Nephi had already decided. He helped himself to a piece of cheese and a peach from Jennifer's plate.

When supper was over they sat talking to Vianah, and at last Jennifer had the chance to ask the question that was always uppermost in her mind. "When these other children—Ollie and the others—were here, how did they get back? You helped them, didn't you? We want you to send us back, too."

"To send you back?" repeated Vianah.

"Yes, back to our own time."

"I am sorry, my children," Vianah said, and for the first time her voice sounded cracked and old. "It was nothing *I* did. It was all their own doing—they had no help from me."

"But Kartan said—"

"I thought *you* knew how they did it," said Kartan. "You once said there was a key. I thought you had it."

"There was some mention of a key, but beyond that I know nothing. They came to me in the old tower not many miles from here."

"Then we've come all this way—all this way—only to find there's no way back," said Jennifer, and she buried her face in her hands, sobbing.

Robert watched her for a few minutes, his face troubled. Then he turned away and looked toward the little house under the peach tree where Alloperla lived.

Jennifer jerked her head up, tears still running

down her cheeks, and when she saw his expression, she shouted, "You don't even care! We're stuck here in this damned place forever—and you don't *even* care!"

# chapter 11

Alloperla tiptoed into the small room at the back of the house to make sure that Kartan and Robert were all right. Satisfied at the sight of them lying on their sleeping mats, breathing evenly, she smiled down at them and left.

After she had gone, Robert stirred restlessly. The sleeping mat was thin and the floor hard, but it was the memory of his quarrel with Jennifer that was keeping him awake. She had yelled at him, right there in the middle of the feast in their honor, and all the brown people had looked bewildered and upset, as if they'd never heard people yelling at each other before. Maybe they hadn't. Some of the children had run away crying.

She had accused him of just being interested in his painting and in finding Duncan, and had said that he didn't care how miserable she was, or that his parents would be worried sick. He *was* interested in painting; but as to finding Duncan, he just wasn't looking anymore. Duncan, with his passion for machinery, wouldn't have fit in here at all—unless he had been captured by the Barbaric Ones.

The unfair part was that she had kept saying that it was all his fault that they hadn't stayed at the stones, where there was at least a chance of getting back. If they *had* stayed at the stones, like she wanted, they would have been caught by the Barbaric Ones. Somehow, the Barbaric Ones seemed less threatening here in Kelso, though Robert knew that Kartan was still worrying about them, and about Savotar and the others who hadn't returned as yet.

Robert finally drifted off to sleep, only to be wakened some time later by voices in the next room. He couldn't make out what was being said, but there seemed to be an urgency to the talk, for the voices were almost shrill.

Unable to contain his curiosity, he reached over and shook Kartan awake.

"There's someone talking in the other room," he whispered. "Who is it?"

"It sounds like Savotar!" said Kartan excitedly, jumping up and pulling on his gray tunic and trousers. "We must find out if they are all safe."

Kartan and Robert burst into the outer room where Savotar, Alloperla, Panchros, and one or two others were talking earnestly over cups of fragrant tea.

"Here is Kartan," Savotar said, rising to his feet. He had to stoop slightly, to avoid a mobile hanging from the ceiling, and his long robe shimmered softly in the candlelight. "We can tell him his part in our plan now. I am afraid that I bring bad news, Kartan. Although we all reached Kelso safely, some of the Barbaric Ones have crossed on rafts from the Far Northlands and their scouts are at this moment close to our town. We had hoped that the difficulty of the currents would save us, but the Barbaric Ones are more determined than we realized."

"What can we do?" Kartan asked.

"We shall send those who are very old, like Vianah, and also the very young, to the tower in the woods, the place that was a stronghold long ago. We have stored a large supply of mealbread and water there so that those who go can remain in hiding until the Barbaric Ones are gone. The rest of us will stay here and talk to them. We hope that if they see us in our town, and understand that our way of life is important to us, they will leave us here. If we fail, and they take us captive, then those who are left—but that is not important now. Your part of the plan is to take Vianah to the tower."

"You mean I am being sent away with the old people and the babies?" Kartan asked. "I would rather stay here with you and meet the Barbaric Ones."

"That I cannot allow," said Savotar firmly. "Alloperla has told me what happened at the Crossing Place. I am not punishing you—that you must understand—but if we are to overcome these Barbaric Ones with the forces of love and trust that we believe in, then only the strongest of our people can be left to meet them."

"Do you not think that I might have learned from what I did at the Crossing Place?" Kartan asked with a trace of bitterness in his voice. "Let me prove it by staying with you."

Savotar shook his head. "Vianah and those children, Robert and Jennifer, need your strength and care."

"Are *they* being sent to the tower, too?"

"Yes, they would be in great danger from the Barbaric Ones and would endanger us, too, for they barely understand the force of love."

"When do we go?" Kartan asked quietly.

"Now, before it is completely light. Lara Avara and several others will accompany the babies and small children to the tower, but I do not think you should travel with them. It is better to travel in small groups. You go with Vianah and these children."

"We will take some mealbread for the journey and then leave," said Kartan.

While Kartan was wrapping portions of mealbread in damp leaves, Robert went through to the back room and took from under his sleeping mat the painting of the Stones of Arden that Kartan had given him. Then he carefully buttoned it inside his shirt. Whatever lay ahead, he wanted to have the painting with him.

As they left the house, Savotar embraced each of

them, and said to Kartan, "Perhaps if I knew what was in store for you, I would not urge you to go, but I feel that you are about to grow in experience and understanding. If you can grow equally in the forces of love and trust, then *you* may one day lead our people."

Jennifer was with Lara Avara at Vianah's house, and Robert dreaded breaking the news that they were once again on the run from the Barbaric Ones. When they got there, however, he found that Nemourah had already told them what was happening, and they were ready to leave.

"I wish you could come with us," Jennifer said to Lara Avara. "Couldn't someone else take the babies?"

"They need everyone who can help. Perhaps you could come with me."

Jennifer hesitated, then said, "No, I'm going with Robert. We have an agreement to stick together."

So Robert knew that the quarrel of the day before was forgotten.

"Then we shall see each other at the tower," Lara Avara said, smiling at Jennifer, her dark eyes bright and her even teeth gleaming in the dim light.

"I've really liked it here, Lara Avara," Jennifer said earnestly. "All that fuss last night was—well—I worry about getting back to my mother and dad. They're my Chosen Ones, you see. I have to get back to them, somehow. Look! In case we don't see each other again, take this thing I found at Norsea." She tried to slip the gold chain and cross over her head, but it caught in her hair. Tugging it free, she slipped it around Lara Avara's neck. The cross gleamed against her brown skin.

"It's real gold," said Robert, thinking that perhaps Lara Avara did not appreciate the extent of Jennifer's generosity.

"It is Jennifer's love that makes the gift valuable," said Vianah softly. "Not the metal from which it is made."

"I'll always wear it," said Lara Avara, hugging Jennifer. "I wish you could always stay here, but I do understand about your Chosen Ones. Meantime, take care of Vianah. Remember, she is *my* Chosen One." Lara Avara turned and ran outside on her way to the Baby House.

The three children led Vianah down the narrow path into the woods. They progressed slowly, for the ground was uneven. Despite their care, Vianah often stumbled and her clothing caught on branches.

"This tower we're going to—it's the same place you met the children from our time, isn't it?" Jennifer asked when they had walked for a while.

"Yes, my people had left me in the tower with mealbread and fuel while they went on their summer journey. But they did not return as soon as I had expected, and I ran out of food. The children came, and two of them—Andrew and Elinor—went to Kelso and brought back food."

Vianah's breath was coming in short gasps from

the effort of walking and talking, and they had to rest for a little before she could go on.

"But don't you know how they got away from the tower?" Jennifer asked.

"No. My people were coming back, and I was afraid that these children would be caught up in the events of our time—just as you have been—and it would be hard for them to leave. I told them that they should go back. They wanted to take me with them," she chuckled.

"And then they just left?" Jennifer persisted.

"They went out the tower door, and I went back inside. There was a scraping sound—perhaps the sound of a key turning in a lock. And then silence, as if time itself had stopped. . . . When the door opened again, Kartan and Lara Avara came rushing in, calling my name. I asked them if they had met the children outside, but they did not know what I was talking about."

Robert and Jennifer dropped a little way behind, leaving Kartan to help Vianah.

"It seems like they were a lot more in control of things than we are," said Robert. "Going off to Kelso and fetching food for her—as if they already knew their way around."

"I know," said Jennifer. "I hate them—dropping in and doing their hero act, then going off home!"

"Of course, we don't know for sure that they did get home," said Robert.

Somehow, that thought wasn't exactly comforting, either.

A sudden shower of rain forced them to shelter under a dense oak tree. Kartan brought out a packet of mealbread, which they shared hungrily.

When the rain stopped, Kartan decided that they should change direction. They followed a stream into the dappled shade of a beechwood. Here the ground was smoother, the walking easier, but with less undergrowth to conceal them, they felt uneasy, always on the alert for the Barbaric Ones. Without Vianah, they could easily have made the journey to the tower in under an hour; as it was, it took them most of the morning. They were slowed down by the numerous streams that dissected this section of the wood, until Kartan and Robert devised a way of clasping their hands to form a chair for carrying Vianah over the wider ones.

At last the trees thinned, and they stepped out of the woods, crossing one final stream. Ahead of them, on a rocky hillside, stood an old square tower built of granite, with cornerstones of red sandstone forming a symmetrical pattern on its tall, straight sides. This tower belonged to a time long before the buildings of Norsea, even before the buildings of Robert and Jennifer's time in Locharden. It was not nearly as old as the stone circle, yet it had that aura of indestructibility, that same feel of having witnessed the passing of time and holding many secrets within its walls.

"It's an old castle, isn't it?" asked Jennifer. "Old in our time, I mean. The kind of thing you pay to go into."

"I think it's a border keep," said Robert. "They were built a long time ago when Scotland was at war with England. We must be in the border country here—we're a long way south of Locharden."

"It's the first thing we've seen that belongs to our time as well as this, since the stones," said Jennifer. "Norsea doesn't count because it was built after our time."

Climbing the rocky hillside to the castle door was the most difficult part of the whole journey for Vianah. In places they had to scramble up the bare, polished rock, and Robert had trouble, too. Jennifer and Kartan helped Vianah up the last slope, then Kartan said he was going back down to gather firewood.

The door of the castle stood wide open, and they looked into the darkness of the bottom room. This lower room must have been a storage cellar, or a place to keep cattle safe in times of attack. It had no windows, the only light coming through the open doorway. Robert stepped inside and saw a spiral staircase winding up within the thickness of one corner of the wall.

"You stay here with Vianah, and I'll see what it's like upstairs," said Robert.

"You're not in charge," said Jennifer. "You should at least wait till Kartan gets here."

"I just want to see what it's like," said Robert and disappeared inside.

Inside the tower, Robert experienced the same feeling he had sometimes noticed at the Stones of Arden. It was almost as if, within these walls, there was a link with things that had happened long ago. As he climbed the spiral stairs this feeling of a link between time now and times past grew within him.

Jennifer, annoyed at Robert for going off, said to Vianah, "We may as well go inside too and get out of the sun."

"Thank you," said the old woman. "It is always pleasantly cool inside the tower, but we will sit in the lower room until Kartan is here to help me up the stairs. In places the steps are crumbling away, and it is a difficult climb even for those with good eyes."

Vianah and Jennifer sat down in a dark corner of the bottom room, looking out of the open door at the rocky hillside that fell away to miles and miles of forested land below.

Robert reached the top of the crumbling staircase and stood in the doorway of the main room of the castle. Part of the roof, high above, had fallen in, letting in the light, and Robert could see the earthen floor and a huge fireplace. To his surprise, a fire was burning. Sitting beside it, like some laird from ancient days, was a bearded, uncouth man. Robert's heart pounded with terror when the man raised his head and stared across the room at him. He was one of the Barbaric Ones—the same man who had chased them twice before, the man they had last seen swimming for his life in the strong currents of the rising tides at the Crossing Place.

He recognized Robert at once, and with a bellow of rage, jumped up and chased him down the stairs. Robert scrambled down the uneven steps, falling rather than running most of the way.

Once outside, Robert threw his weight against the heavy oak door and it began to swing shut. In the instant before it closed, Robert caught sight of Jennifer's frightened face, framed by untidy hair, staring back at him from the dim interior of the bottom room. He saw her only for a fraction of a second, but the image was stamped indelibly on his mind.

Before he had a chance to pull the door open again, Kartan, who had been dragging a large branch up the last steep slope, sprang to his side and put his hand on a key, a shining key, which was sticking out of the lock.

"Don't do it!" Robert screamed.

But the key turned, almost without any effort from Kartan at all.

Inside, they heard Jennifer start to scream, but the scream was cut off by silence—a silence so intense that it seemed to arrest their heartbeats and still the pulse of life within them.

And then sound once again filled the void—the distant clatter of a truck rattling along a rough road, a dog barking, and a small voice asking persistently, "Where did you come from?"

With disbelieving eyes, Robert looked around him. The forest had dissolved, and from the rocky hill on which the tower stood, Robert could see a great patchwork of fields and farms, a small pond half overgrown with rushes, and a cottage down near a road. He caught a glimpse of a milk truck as it passed along the road between the hedges.

And still the persistent voice asked, "Who are you? Where did you come from?"

Robert looked at Kartan, standing beside him, his eyes blank with fear. Robert felt the same fear welling up within him as he asked, "What has happened to Jennifer?"

"Open the door! Open the door quickly and find out!"

# chapter 12

Ignoring the small blond girl sitting on the rock near the tower, Robert put his hand on the key, which was still in the door. It was black now, not shining as it had been before, and it was stiff to turn.

"You can't get back again," said the girl.

But Robert did not hear her. He turned the key, pulled open the door, and stepped inside.

"Jennifer! Jennifer! Vianah!" he shouted, and the echo of his cry in the empty tower taunted him. He felt his way up the spiral staircase to the upper room, calling Jennifer's name; but neither Jennifer, Vianah, or the Barbaric One was there to answer him.

Very slowly he came back downstairs and stepped outside. Judging by the position of the sun and the thin mist hanging over the pond, it was very early in the morning.

"Did you find her?" asked the small child eagerly.

Robert shook his head. He looked at Kartan and then at the girl, totally confused.

"But you *were* with her?" she asked.

"With whom?" Robert asked dully.

"Vianah, of course! I heard you calling to her."

Robert now gave his full attention to the untidy fair-haired child sitting on the rock. She was eating a bun and had sticky crumbs all around her mouth.

"You know Vianah?" he asked. "Who *are* you, anyway?"

He had to wait while she crammed the last of the bun into her mouth and chewed it before she answered.

"We saw Vianah a long time ago. Andrew and Elinor hardly believe it anymore, but I'm sure Ian does."

"Are you Ollie? But you can't be—you're too young."

"I'm six, nearly seven," said Ollie indignantly. "What do you mean—too young?"

"But Vianah didn't say that you were just a little kid. She always spoke like you were—"

"What's wrong with being a little kid?" Ollie asked, sounding as if she might cry.

"It's just that I'm surprised," said Robert. "Don't bawl! You've been to that other time? You know how to get there and back?"

Ollie nodded. "The key did it."

"Can you make it do it again? I have to go back there."

"For Vianah?"

"No, for Jennifer. She was there with me, and I have to take Kartan back."

Kartan had been staring at them both with blank eyes. Even the news that this was Ollie, of whom Vianah had so often spoken, did not seem to penetrate his mind.

"He's one of Vianah's brown people, isn't he?" Ollie asked, smiling at Kartan. "I'm glad you've come."

"Can you show me how to work the key?"

Ollie shook her head. "You can't *work* it. You just have to wait for it to happen."

"But you got back here before, using the key."

"It's not glowing anymore," said Ollie, as if that explained everything. "It's just a key now."

"Look here," said Robert urgently. "Are the others—Andrew and so on—older than you?"

"Oh yes," said Ollie. "Andrew is thirteen."

"Can you bring him here? I've got to talk to him."

"He's in London. All the others are in London."

"London? What on earth are they doing there?"

"We live in London?"

"Then what are *you* doing here?"

"Aunt Grace is sick. She lives down there in Smailholm Cottage and she keeps the key to Smailholm Tower in a box by her back door. When she got sick my mother had to come and look after her. The others all stayed in London with Dad because of school, but my mother brought me along. I can miss school--I'm a very good reader," she added a little smugly.

"And you were all here before—when you went to see Vianah?" Robert asked.

Ollie nodded. "That was last year. Andrew hardly believes it anymore, it was so strange, but even he made me promise that if the key did begin to glow again—that's how it was when we unlocked the tower and found Vianah there—I wasn't to use it."

"And it did begin to glow?"

"Yes. I woke up very early this morning and I remembered I'd left my brother's paddleboat out by the pond. He let me bring it, but he made me promise to look after it, so I got out of bed and came out to find it. When I passed the box by the back door, where Aunt Grace keeps the key to the tower—"

"Why does *she* keep the key?" Robert interrupted.

"So tourists can see the castle. It's her job to keep the key. Anyway, I peeked at the key, like I always do, and it was sort of glowing. I'd promised not to use it—but I didn't promise not to put it in the lock. So I was just sitting waiting to see if anyone would come along, and then suddenly you were there! I hadn't expected anyone to come from *inside* the tower."

Robert stood leaning against the granite wall of the tower, thinking this over. "What day is it?" he asked, at last.

"Friday, I think. It's hard to remember when there's no school."

"What Friday?"

"About the twenty-second of June. Mother said yesterday was the longest day, and it seemed like it—not having anyone to play with and having to keep so quiet because Aunt Grace is sick."

"But that's impossible—"

"You keep asking me questions and then not believing the answers."

"But that would mean—that would mean no time has passed," Robert said slowly. "It's impossible. And they wouldn't have missed us yet."

"But it's true," said Ollie. "Aunt Grace didn't miss *us*."

"If there was just someone I could talk to!" said Robert. "I wish your brother was here."

Ollie glowered, and Robert realized he wasn't being tactful. It was a miracle that he'd found Ollie, and the others probably didn't understand much more than she did. In an obscure way it comforted him to know that *they* hadn't been in control either. They had apparently just blundered through on some sort of instinct. Maybe he could, too.

It was then that he thought of returning to the Stones of Arden.

"Where exactly are we?" Robert asked Ollie.

"This is Smailholm Tower, near Kelso."

"Kelso!" echoed Robert, excited at hearing a familiar name.

"It's not the same Kelso, though. Andrew has been to them both, and he said that they're not the same."

Just then they saw a car on the road that wound past Aunt Grace's cottage at the bottom of the hill. Kartan, who had shown no interest in their conversation, scrambled onto a rock and watched it until it was out of sight, half excited, half afraid.

"It was a car, wasn't it?" he asked, wide-eyed with wonder. "I never thought I would see one!"

"Maybe you could even ride in one," said Robert.

"And travel faster than birds can fly!" whispered Kartan.

Kartan's excitement lightened Robert's mood. It might be fun to take him on a tour of the twentieth century. There would be even more for him to see than there had been for Robert to see in Kartan's time.

"We'll go in a car," Robert promised firmly. "We'll hitchhike back to Locharden."

"In those funny clothes?" Ollie asked, looking at Kartan's loose gray pants and embroidered tunic and cloak.

Robert had become so used to Kartan's clothes that he had overlooked how his outfit would look in present-day Kelso, especially on a boy hitchhiking. Hitchhiking, itself, would provide enough problems without that.

"I could get you a pair of Andrew's jeans and a shirt," Ollie offered.

"But he's in London," Robert pointed out.

"He left a pair of jeans here last year that were too small, and there's a shirt of Elinor's that might do. They're in a drawer in my bedroom. I'll get them."

When Ollie came back and Kartan put on the jeans and shirt, he looked far less conspicuous. Now that he had recovered from the fright of finding himself in the twentieth century he was interested in all that he could see, but a plane sent him ducking for cover, and although it was high overhead, he was greatly distressed by the noise. ("Lucky he didn't arrive at London Airport," Ollie remarked.) While jeans and a shirt might make him stand out less, they wouldn't turn him into a twentieth-century boy. Someone who cowered at the sound of a plane, or thought that a zipper was a miracle, wasn't going to pass as an average citizen.

"Why do you have to go?" asked Ollie, watching Robert bundling Kartan's clothes inside his cloak. "You haven't even told me about Vianah yet."

"We have to try and get back to Kartan's time," said Robert, and then told Ollie how Jennifer had been left there.

Ollie was very upset to hear of the arrival of the Barbaric Ones and of Vianah's danger, but to Robert, all that was nothing compared to the thought that Jennifer had been left behind. They had promised to stick together. . . .

"Look, I've *got* to leave now," he declared. "It's not like time's standing still anymore. Soon they'll be out looking for us, and I've got to reach Jennifer first."

Rather reluctantly, Ollie pointed out the direction to Kelso, then decided to walk some of the way with them. Robert was impressed by how much she knew and remembered about her visit to Vianah. There could be no doubt that she'd been there.

"I'll have to go back," she said at last. "It must be nearly breakfast time."

That thought made Robert hungry. He wished that he had some mealbread to share with Kartan. Kartan was too busy asking questions to think about food. The road under his feet, the telephone wires overhead, a long straight wall, and a sign beside the road showing the Kelso coat of arms, all prompted a stream of questions, most of which Robert couldn't answer. How *do* voices travel through telephone wires and where are road signs made? In a road sign factory, he wondered?

Although there was little traffic so early in the day, those cars that they did see alarmed Kartan by their speed and noise. When they got nearer the town, Kartan was amazed at the number of people, the height of the buildings, and all the traffic.

"Wait till you see Edinburgh!" Robert told him. "You'll see double-decker buses and hundreds of cars and lorries and trucks. At the corner of the streets they have red and green lights so that the cars know when it's their turn to go."

But Kartan was too impressed by the sights and sounds around him to try and imagine anything more overwhelming.

When they reached the market square, even Robert was surprised by the number of people. Three buses were lined up in the parking lot and the streets were seething with children. It must be some sort of school outing, he decided. Finding himself next to a small boy with rabbitlike front teeth, he asked, "Where are you all going?"

"To the castle and the zoo," the boy told him.

"In Edinburgh?"

"Aye."

"And all these kids are going?" Robert asked.

"Aye."

"And the teachers?"

The boy nodded. "It's just for people from our school, though."

"Do they count you?"

"They'll likely count us after we're in the bus."

"My friend and I—we're trying to get to Edinburgh. Do you think you could get us on the bus?"

"Are you runnin' away?" the boy asked, and there was a hint of respect in his voice.

"Sort of," said Robert.

"You'd have to sit on the floor," said the boy. "Hey, Dick, here's two boys runnin' away. Do you think we could get them on the bus?"

"We'd need to get them past Fish-face first," said the other boy. "We could hide them if we sat near the back."

"Fish-face?"

"Mr. Fisher, the teacher." Dick inclined his head

toward a tall man with thin hair combed carefully across his balding head. He was standing near the bus checking lists and counting lunches.

Just then he looked up from his lists and called out, "Will all the children in my class get into the first bus, and I'll count you after you're seated."

The children in Mr. Fisher's class surged forward into the bus. Robert caught hold of Kartan's shirt sleeve and pulled him along with the crowd of pushing boys and girls.

"Take it easy," said Mr. Fisher, but made no move to control the pushing children so that Robert and Kartan found themselves inside the bus, unnoticed by the teacher. They were soon spirited away to seats near the back, where Dick—who was a take-charge sort—told them to get down on the floor. He ordered some other boys to throw their coats over Robert and Kartan so that if Fish-face came up the aisle he wouldn't notice them. There was so much cooperation that Kartan and Robert were all but smothered under the pile of coats and jackets.

Robert wished he had had more time to brief Kartan on what was happening. So far, Kartan had been so overcome by fright that he had not spoken, but Robert knew that the moment the bus started up, Kartan would say something that would give away the fact that he had never been in a bus before. He was just about to suggest to Kartan that he should pretend to be dumb and let him do all the speaking, when the bus started with a lurch. Dick jerked away the jackets and told Robert to cross the aisle to the seats opposite. "There's more room with Eric and John. David and I have nowhere to put our feet with both of you here," Dick told them.

Eric and John were full of questions about where Robert was running from and where he was going to, and once again Robert wished he had given some thought to what he was going to tell people.

All attention was suddenly diverted from Robert when Dick said, "Hey! This kid's from the future and his name's Kartan!"

By now all the children in the back half of the bus knew that they had two extra passengers aboard. Kartan's remarks spread quickly among them.

"It's his first ride in a bus!"

"He says there's no cars in the future." This news was received with a considerable amount of dismay and disbelief, but someone supported Kartan by saying, "My dad said that all the petrol is going to be used up by about the year 2000."

Robert didn't see how they could possibly accept that Kartan came from the future, yet they were all willing to go along with the idea. They seemed to want to believe it. They were fascinated by him—and he was different enough from them in appearance, even without his embroidered tunic, to make his claim seem faintly possible. His high, singsong voice contrasted with their broad Scottish voices. So they listened to his stories and plied him with questions. They were delighted to instruct him in every technological triumph of the twentieth century. They dug into their pockets and brought out bubblegum, which was as much a miracle to him as a tiny pocket transistor radio.

One boy gave him a green plastic whistle. "You can keep it," he told Kartan earnestly, and Kartan accepted it as if it were a great treasure, like the gold cross Jennifer had given Lara Avara.

Mr. Fisher was aware of a hum of excitement at the back of the bus, but assigned it to the prospect of a day away from school. The children were careful to keep their noise below the point at which Fish-face would come to the back to see what was going on.

"Are you going to the castle or the zoo first?" Robert asked Eric.

"The castle this morning and the zoo this afternoon," he answered.

It would have been better if it had been the other way around, Robert thought to himself. The zoo was on the other side of Edinburgh, and they needed to get there. He wasn't sure how they would get through the city without money for bus fares.

"You can come with us," one of the boys said.

"Kartan's never seen an elephant!" said another. "We've got to show him an elephant!"

Nearly all the children had been to both the castle and the zoo many times before, so they weren't nearly as excited about that as they were about having Kartan and Robert along. Kartan's enthusiasm and amazement had won them over, not to mention the fun of fooling Fish-face for a whole day.

"Once we're out of the bus he'll know we don't belong," said Robert. "He'll see us!"

"He'll think you're kids from another class or even another school," said Dick. "There's no law to stop you walking around the zoo near our class. It's a public place."

"But we should be getting along," said Robert.

"Kartan says you're going back to the future. There's no hurry because, when you get there, it won't be the future," said Dick, laughing at his own wit.

Robert was still worried, but he had no alternative plan. In the end, he decided to stay with the schoolchildren. When the bus stopped on the castle esplanade they had no trouble getting out while Mr. Fisher was talking to the driver, and then Kartan and Robert went around with separate groups of children. Dick insisted on that.

They visited St. Margaret's Chapel, peered into a great cannon called Mons Meg, and looked down on a graveyard for soldiers' dogs with sad epitaphs on tiny tombstones. They toured a museum full of old-fashioned uniforms and swords and muskets. Mr. Fisher had never had a more interested group of children in his charge than he had that day. Kartan was full of questions, many of which the children could not answer, so they asked Mr. Fisher.

Before getting back on the bus, box lunches were

149

passed out to the children by the teachers—along with a lecture about not littering. Kartan and Robert, of course, didn't get any lunches, but a small, thin girl called Rena gave hers to Kartan, saying that she would get bus-sick if she ate it. They were also showered with bags of potato chips, chocolate bars, apples, and gum.

"It is better than mealbread!" said Kartan smiling, as he bit into a bar of chocolate.

Kartan seemed to be accepting the adventures of the day so casually that Robert found himself growing annoyed. He had been left with the whole responsibility of finding the way back to Locharden and the stones, and Kartan was giving no thought to what would happen when they finally got there. It was all Robert could do not to remind Kartan of some of the problems they still had to face.

When it was time to get back on the bus, Mr. Fisher was a little surprised by the children's eagerness to get to the zoo. Several times he overheard children say, "I just can't wait to get to the elephants," or, "Won't it be great at the monkey's tea party?"

When the bus finally stopped, Mr. Fisher made a short speech, telling them they were allowed to wander around by themselves, but they must be back at the aquarium by the main gate at four o'clock. They would tour it together—until then, they were on their own.

"Which way to the elephants?" Dick Chapman

asked Mr. Fisher as they swarmed out the bus, nearly knocking him down.

Mr. Fisher gestured weakly and watched in dismay as thirty children—thirty-two if he had had time to count them—went stampeding off in search of the elephants.

"Imagine getting so excited over an elephant," he muttered to himself, shaking his head. Then he found a quiet corner near the polar bears, where he could sit and rest until four o'clock.

# chapter 13

The motorway was busy with evening traffic, but no one paid any attention to two boys trudging along the grass verge. Kartan was worn out after the excitement of the long day. Confused images of elephants and tigers, and crowns sparkling with jewels, and weapons of war all flooded his mind. In a special room in the castle he had seen rows of books, all filled with the names of people who had died in what they called World War II. Some of the children had found the names of their grandfathers and uncles, and they hadn't been sad or fearful. They had acted proud, as if dying in a war was a good thing. Kartan thought this twentieth century a strange world, and the noise and speed of the cars on the great roadway left him dazed and numb. They came and they came and they never stopped coming.

Robert, too, was very tired. He was now regretting the hours they had wasted at the castle and the zoo.

Although it would remain light for some time, he was uneasy about accepting a ride this late in the evening. No one was stopping anyway.

He wondered what his mother was doing. He should have been home from school some time ago, so by now she must be wondering where he was. Jennifer's mother probably missed her in the morning, and would have been worrying all day. "Her Chosen One," Jennifer had called her mother. Thinking of Jennifer brought back the terrible feeling of hopelessness. How was he going to explain where she was? And what had happened to her since he left? She hadn't been at ease there, even when things were going well. Now, trapped in the tower with a Barbaric One . . . .

He tried to push the thought away by concentrating on his immediate problems. He was hungry again and didn't have a convenient package of mealbread to offer Kartan. Soon they had to cross the Forth Road Bridge. It was a toll bridge, and he didn't know if pedestrians had to pay. Even if they didn't, there would likely be questions as to why two boys were crossing the bridge on foot at this time of night. They just had to get a ride.

Some distance down the road he could see the lights of a gas station, and a plan began to take shape in his mind. Perhaps they could get a ride without having to ask. They could climb onto the back of a truck while the driver was buying gas and take a chance that it was going in the right direction. Almost anything traveling along this road would be going across the bridge, and that had become his immediate goal.

A rather untidy beech hedge separated the gas station from a field, and Robert decided that they could hide behind the hedge and from there see what the prospects were for a ride. So they crawled into the field and, partly screened by foliage, they waited.

A car pulled in, and a youth in his late teens with long black hair and dirty overalls came out and attended to the car. Something about the boy caught Robert's attention, though he was not sure what it was. Robert watched regretfully as the car pulled away, giving them no chance to get near it.

No more cars stopped for a long time. Kartan fell asleep. Robert was growing sleepy too, lulled by the drone of traffic on the highway and music from a transistor radio playing in the garage. He struggled to stay awake. He must not miss the chance of a ride.

The music stopped abruptly, and Robert could hear a voice reading a summary of the local news. He was scarcely listening, but snapped to attention when the voice on the radio began to read a missing-persons bulletin. Two children, aged eleven and twelve, were missing in the Locharden area. Robert Guthrie, eleven, had not been seen since going to bed the evening before. He was small for his age, had dark curly hair and brown eyes, and walked with a noticeable limp. Robert glowered at the description. It wasn't a noticeable limp—only when he was tired. Jennifer Crandall, twelve, had long red hair. She was American. A volunteer search party was out on the moor, north of Locharden, and a helicopter was standing by. Dense fog covered the area and the helicopter could not be used until it cleared. The weather conditions were unusual, as the fog was very localized.

The youth in the garage had apparently turned up the volume of the radio during the announcement, and the voice blared out above the steady hum of the traffic.

How would they get back unnoticed now, Robert wondered. After that bulletin people would be suspicious if they saw two boys hitchhiking—even if it had said a boy and a girl.

Then Robert realized that there was really no difficulty about getting back to Locharden. He could simply walk into any police station, and he would be taken home quick enough. But how could he explain Jennifer's disappearance, and Kartan's presence? If the police found him, without Jennifer, then it was going to lead to all sorts of questions to which there were no answers. No, he and Kartan had to reach the stone circle and solve this for themselves—if there was any solution. Robert shivered.

It was almost dark, and suddenly became darker, when the youth switched off the lighted sign above the gas station. He was closing up for the night. No more cars would be stopping until morning, and tomorrow they would still be faced with the problem of crossing the toll bridge.

Then Robert heard him start up a car around the

back somewhere and suddenly panicked. The thought of spending the night under the hedge, with all these worries still to face tomorrow, completely unnerved him. Rousing Kartan, he said, "Come on! We'll see if that guy out there will give us a ride over the bridge, if he's going that way. It will be better than staying here all night."

Kartan, still groggy with sleep, swayed on his feet as Robert helped him out of the bushes onto the paved area near the gas pumps. When the car came around the side of the garage the two boys stood there, clearly visible in the car's headlights. At the last minute, Robert lost his nerve and dived back into the cover of the bushes, but Kartan stood still, pinned in the headlights like a frightened animal, too puzzled to run.

"Who are you?" asked a voice from behind the light. "What are you up to?"

The older boy stepped out of the car. "Where's the other one? I saw him run."

Reluctantly, Robert came out of hiding. The boy gave a low whistle and then asked, "How the hell did you get here?"

Robert stood, hunched as if ready to run, but the boy reached out and caught him by the shoulder and pulled him closer.

"You *are* Robert, aren't you?" he asked.

Robert swallowed nervously, then nodded. So the boy *had* been paying attention to the radio announcer.

"You haven't changed much—maybe grown some. Don't you know me?"

Robert turned his thoughts away from his own predicament and really looked at the boy who was talking to him. Take away the long hair and the slight growth of stubble on the chin and a scar on his eyebrow. It was—it had to be—

"Duncan?" asked Robert in a tremulous voice.

The boy laughed. "It's me, all right! And you didn't even know your own brother!"

Taking a cigarette from the pocket of his greasy overalls, the boy said, "But what are you up to? You're too young to run away, Robert. How old are you? Eleven? And I suppose this is the other kid they talked about."

Duncan lit a cigarette and took a long pull on it. "I was fourteen and that was bad enough," he said. "A kid like you couldn't make it. I'm going to have to take you home."

"We want to go back," said Robert quietly. "But you won't tell the police, will you?"

"Of course not! What's it to do with them? But I'll have to make a phone call first. Can I trust you not to run off? You'd better come in with me so that I can keep an eye on you."

Robert felt rather the same way. Having found Duncan, he didn't want him to vanish again, and was quite glad to follow him into the garage.

"I'll have to get this guy to pick up the key and run

the pumps for me tomorrow. I'll tell him I'll be gone for a day or two, maybe longer, till we see how things are around home."

Robert climbed into the car next to Duncan, and pulled Kartan in beside him. He didn't want to have to explain any strange remark Kartan might make. Duncan wasn't going to accept the "boy from the future talk" the way the boys on the bus did.

In no time at all they had crossed the great bridge. Kartan, still utterly wearied by the events of the day, slept. Duncan drove fast and expertly, giving most of his attention to the road. Even when they turned off the motorway onto narrow roads, he did not slow down.

When they were finally getting near familiar country, Duncan asked abruptly, "How are they?"

"Mum and Dad?" asked Robert.

Duncan nodded, keeping his eyes on the road straight ahead.

"All right, I suppose," said Robert slowly. "It hasn't been the same since you went away, Duncan. They're worried all the time. And I have to do all your work as well as my own." There was a hint of a whine in Robert's voice.

Duncan looked at him sharply. "That's why you ran off, I suppose," he said, giving his attention to driving again.

"I didn't run away. . . . I sort of got lost."

"Oh, sure!" said Duncan sarcastically. "You were out on the moor looking for Dad's sheep and you got lost somehow and turned up on the motorway by the Forth Bridge."

Robert bit his lip and could think of nothing to say.

"I don't blame you. After all, that was why I ran away."

"I thought it was because of wrecking the motor-bike," said Robert, and then wished he hadn't brought that up.

"That was just part of it," said Duncan. "It was mostly because I got tired of working all the time. At least for him. . . . Does he still get mad?"

"Sometimes," answered Robert.

"Was he mad when I ran away?"

"Not mad," said Robert, trying to find the right words to express it. "He was sorry."

"And yet *you* ran away, too."

"I don't want him to think I ran away," Robert pleaded. "It would be better for him if he just thought I was lost on the moor. Would you let me out before we reach the farm?"

"And give you the chance to run away again?"

"I wouldn't! Honestly, I wouldn't!" said Robert. "There's something I have to do first. Jennifer's still out on the moor. I have to find her."

"The American girl? Then who's this kid?"

"He's going to help me find her. She's out there somewhere."

"I'm not going home unless I can take you with me," said Duncan firmly.

"You could say that you heard on the news that I

was lost and you wanted to help look for me. They'd be pleased if you did that."

Robert looked at Duncan's grave profile, but was unable to read his thoughts. By this time they were driving through Locharden, the headlights of the car silhouetting the dark sleeping cottages against the moor. Then they swung onto the road that led to Baldry. Duncan turned sharply onto the road up past the Taylor Farm toward their place. There were lights on in the Taylor Farm.

"O.K., where do you want out?" asked Duncan.

"This is fine," said Robert.

Duncan braked sharply. "I'm taking an awful chance, but there's something going on that I don't understand. You'd better not let me down."

Robert shook Kartan awake. They climbed out of the car and stood together on the road, watching the taillights as the car wound up the hill to the Guthrie farm.

"Where are we going now?" Kartan asked.

Robert didn't answer but led the way along the narrow sheep path that wound up toward the black shape of Ben Arden. He wished that he could have been there to see the happy disbelief in his parents' eyes when Duncan arrived home—but there was Jennifer to think about. Resolutely he plodded on, hoping that he could reach the Stones of Arden before the searchers found them. Even after all that had happened, he felt a tingle of anticipation at the thought of seeing the stones again.

# chapter 14

Jennifer and Vianah, sitting in the dark bottom room of the tower, heard the agitated sound of footsteps running down the stairs, and Jennifer saw Robert silhouetted against the light before the door slammed shut. Then there were more footsteps, heavy footsteps, and Jennifer screamed. The scream died in her throat as a slight scraping sound came from the direction of the door. The sound of a key turning in the lock? Then silence. Frightening, empty silence. And cold. . . .

Jennifer clutched at Vianah and could feel Vianah's frail body rigid in her arms. They were shut inside the tower, and someone was there with them. She could hear his heavy breathing and shuffling feet. He was pounding on the door, and then let forth a stream of harsh words in a language that she could not understand. Suddenly, the door burst open, and light flooded the pitch-black room. Even from the brief glimpse she had of him before he disappeared outside, Jennifer recognized him.

"It's one of the Barbaric Ones," she whispered to Vianah. "It's one of the men we thought had drowned at the Crossing Place. He's gone outside after Robert. Robert was running away from him."

"He will not find Robert," said Vianah softly.

"He'll catch him," said Jennifer. "You see, Robert can't run very fast—he's lame. On the rocks he won't stand a chance."

"I think Robert has escaped," said Vianah slowly. "Back to his own time."

It took a few minutes for Vianah's words to sink into Jennifer's brain, and when she finally understood what Vianah had said, she rejected it angrily. "He couldn't have done that—not without me! And how would you know? You can't see anything—you're blind."

"The blind use other senses," said Vianah, still talking gently. "There was a sound—like a key turning in a lock—that I have heard before. And the silence, the cold, the waiting. That was how I knew that Ollie and the others were gone."

"So you *did* have something to do with it!"

"No! They did it all by themselves. I had no part in it."

"But I want to go back, too!"

"You must be patient, child. Your turn will come. But for now, what are we going to do? When the

Barbaric One does not find Robert and Kartan he will return here and find us."

"Kartan? Has he gone, too?" wailed Jennifer.

"I do not know—but they were out there together."

Jennifer stared numbly out of the open doorway, unable to accept what had happened. She was alone, trapped in this other time, forsaken by Robert and even Kartan. Her only companion was a blind old woman, and soon the Barbaric One would come back. Although Vianah urged Jennifer to hide, she did nothing. She stayed where she was, leaning against the cold stone wall of the tower, a shadowy figure in the dimly lit room, waiting for the uncouth bearded man to find her.

Jennifer registered no surprise when, instead, a crowd of people came bursting through the doorway, talking together in excited voices. There were several men and women carrying babies, and a large number of small children. Lara Avara was with them, holding little Nephi by the hand.

"Jennifer, Vianah! You reached here first!" Lara Avara broke away from Nephi and came running over to Vianah and hugged her. She was about to embrace Jennifer, too, but stopped and said, "There is something wrong. What has happened?"

"Robert and Kartan have gone," Vianah explained in a tired voice. "And one of the Barbaric Ones has found us here."

As she said these words the shadow of the huge bearded man darkened the doorway.

Jennifer watched the meeting between the Barbaric One and Vianah's people in a completely detached way. She no longer cared what happened, and when they invited him to the upstairs room and shared mealbread and water with him, she followed them, but did not even try to understand what was happening.

One of the younger men knew some of the Barbaric One's guttural language and spoke with him briefly. Then he held a long, earnest conversation with his own people. Lara Avara took part in the discussion, giving anxious, sidelong glances in Jennifer's direction.

At last, Lara Avara came over to Jennifer and asked, "Have you been listening to our talk?"

Jennifer shook her head.

"The Bearded One wants you to go with him to Kelso."

"But I don't know how to get there," Jennifer answered dully.

"It is not difficult—follow the river."

"Then let him find it himself."

"We told him that," said Lara Avara in a worried voice. "He insists that you go, too."

"Why me?"

Lara Avara nervously pleated the hem of her tunic between her fingers. Her face had lost its customary peaceful expression and she looked at Jennifer with tears welling up in her eyes.

"He wants to take you as a hostage to guarantee his safety if he meets more of our people. He cannot understand that he needs no hostage. Our people will not harm him. I have begged to go in your place, but he will not listen."

Jennifer looked at Lara Avara's tear-stained face and said, "I'll go. It doesn't make any difference what happens now. I'm not even frightened of him anymore."

The parting from Lara Avara, Vianah, and the others meant nothing to Jennifer, although little Nephi clung to her tearfully, begging her to stay. Mercifully the journey back to Kelso with the Bearded One, as Lara Avara and the others called him, was also just a blur. Jennifer stumbled along, ignoring his meaningless words and his cruelty. It was only when she was at the edge of the clearing, looking at the town, that the thought came to her that she was disloyal to lead a Barbaric One right to the heart of their peaceful settlement. But he would have found his way there anyway, she told herself. They had told him that it was farther up the river.

Savotar came out to meet them, looking down at Jennifer with great compassion. Her face was drained of color, and smeared with tears, and blood crusted a gash on her forehead. Whether the wound had been from a trailing branch or a blow from the Barbaric One she could not remember.

"I'm sorry," Jennifer said hoarsely. "I shouldn't have let him come here."

"You had no choice. And it makes no difference," said Savotar sadly. "The Barbaric Ones have already found us. At this moment they are taking prisoners and looting our town. They would not listen to our carefully prepared words. They have not even sat down with us."

Jennifer, still in a state of shock, was left with only a hazy recollection of the next few hours. Nemourah cleaned her up and bathed her forehead, then gave her some sweet herb tea. For a little while she slept.

Evening came. The Barbaric Ones had taken their prisoners and marched them out of the town. A long column of people, hands tied behind their backs. Among them were Savotar, Nemourah, Alloperla, Panchros, and Jennifer. She was the only child.

They marched, they slept, they shared their meal-bread with the Barbaric Ones. When they came to the Crossing Place, Jennifer was sure that Savotar would have some plan for escape, and even spoke to him about it.

"Patience, child," he said. "You are only making it harder for yourself with your anger and bitterness."

"And you only make it easy for them," said Jennifer angrily. "You don't stick up for yourself at all."

What Savotar said was true. Jennifer did make it harder for herself. The Barbaric Ones found these tall brown people so passive and friendly that they relaxed their watchfulness. They no longer tied their hands, and in the evening everyone sat around the fire together. Only Jennifer sulked, taking every chance she could to annoy them.

As they walked through the never ending woods, flanked by the Barbaric Ones, Jennifer began to find Savotar's company almost as trying as the Barbaric Ones'. Savotar was worried about her, she could see that. But he was so preachy! Always telling her that if she just showed more love and patience, they wouldn't be so mean to her.

That morning she had tried, and it hadn't worked. For more than an hour she had done nothing to annoy the Bearded One, but still he had struck her twice.

In the afternoon—it was now the third day since they had left Kelso—they reached the rhododendron woods, and the sinister atmosphere of the place rubbed Jennifer's nerves raw. She spoke rudely to Savotar, and after that she tried to avoid him, but she knew that he was keeping an eye on her. Then she stumbled on a root, and the Bearded One, ever watchful, flicked her with his stick and told her to hurry along.

"I'm tired," she said. "I can't go any farther!"

Jennifer stood in front of him, looking up defiantly. In her misery she had again lost her fear. She didn't care what happened.

The Barbaric One raised his stick to strike her. Jennifer cringed, waiting for the blow. But the blow never came. Savotar—Savotar who preached love and patience—snatched the stick from the bearded man's hand and began to beat him.

167

"Run, child! Run!" he shouted. "Find your way back to your own people. Back where you belong!"

Jennifer was never to forget the look on Savotar's face as he struck the Barbaric One. It was as hard for him, schooled in generations of peace, to raise a weapon in anger as it was for her to restrain her hate.

In the confusion that followed the fight between Savotar and the Barbaric One, Jennifer ducked into the trees and ran until she could run no farther. At last, sinking to her knees among the brown, leathery leaves, she rested. The wood was very quiet. A faint mist swirled through the trees, almost like wisps of blue smoke. The hated Barbaric Ones were gone, but so were the gentle brown people—and Vianah and Lara Avara and Robert and Kartan. She, Jennifer Crandall, was completely alone.

The silence was oppressive. There was that strange atmosphere of the lifeless woods—the uniformity of the trees, the lack of plants growing in their shade, the complete absence of birds and animals. And, always, the waiting silence.

Jennifer was thoroughly frightened and wished she had not left Savotar. She would go back and find him. Anything was better than being alone. She began to run aimlessly through the trees, calling his name. She became even more frightened and confused when everything was blotted out in thick, suffocating fog.

Something loomed out of the mist in front of her, and stretching out her hands, she grazed her knuckles on one of the big, standing stones. She had found the stone circle. The Circle of Time. Unable to go farther, she fell to her knees and began with what little strength remained in her to tear at the grass and roots, pulling up handfuls of soil.

# chapter 15

Kartan undid the bundle of clothes, which he was still carrying, and wrapped his gray cloak tightly around him. Beside him, Robert shivered inside his jacket, partly from cold and partly from excitement. The huge stones were visible now, the only solid features in the shadowy landscape of swirling mists. The waiting silence was shattered by the plaintive cry of a sea bird, and to Robert's ears it sounded like the voice of Jennifer calling to him through the mists of time.

He stepped into the gap between two stones and once again the cold clamminess of the mist reached into his mind. Suddenly he longed for the warmth and beauty of the land of the brown people. He wanted once again to hear their high voices, to study their paintings, to understand their belief in peace and love and sharing.

The sea bird screamed again, and another answered it faintly, an echo in the mist. It was then that Robert faced the truth. He hadn't come all this way just to take Kartan back, or to try to find Jennifer. All he really wanted was to reach the brown people. The brown people had claimed him as one of their own. Even finding Duncan again didn't change anything. In a way it helped, because his parents would have Duncan now. . . .

Robert turned to Kartan, who was staring at the stones, his eyes round with fear and his brown face sallow in the strange half-light of the mist. Pointing across the circle to the third gap, Kartan said in a broken voice, "That is where they buried my Chosen Brother, Aetherix." Then he ran across the circle, stumbling and tripping on the coarse heather. Sinking to his knees, he began to tear at the turf. It was the way he had been when Robert first saw him—a gray-cloaked figure, kneeling between the stones sobbing.

Robert sank down where he was and began to dig slowly, without conscious will. Gradually, his mind became too numb with cold to know what he did. The cold, the silence, intensified. The mist grew more dense, shutting out the rest of the stones in the circle. Time stood still.

Then Robert was aware of warmth and light and sound again—the sound of waves breaking on the shore. He opened his eyes and saw the thick growth of rhododendrons pressing in around the stone circle, their leaves rattling slightly in a passing breeze. Suddenly he was gripped by a deep, searing pain, almost as if he was being torn apart. The leaves on the bushes danced wildly, and then blurred, out of focus. The pounding waves roared in his ears. He lost consciousness.

When he came to, he thought he could still hear the pounding waves, but gradually that sound was replaced by an insistent voice calling his name. "Robert! Robert! Are you all right?" Someone was shaking him. Why couldn't they leave him alone, let him stay where he wanted to be, where he really belonged?

"Robert, speak to me!"

Reluctantly, Robert opened his eyes to find Jennifer bending over him, her red hair falling across her face like an untidy red curtain. She pushed it back from her eyes and he saw a deep scar on her forehead.

"Your head—how did you hurt your head?" he asked.

Jennifer touched the scar and drew her fingers away quickly.

"We're back! We're safe, Robert," she said.

Cautiously Robert looked around and saw that Kartan was no longer there. The mists were melting in the rising sun, clinging only to the damp, low places on the moor. The massive hulk of Ben Arden towered behind them, and the moor looked strangely peaceful in the dawn light. Shakily, he rose to his feet, and the two of them walked away from the stones.

They plodded on in silence for some time, before Jennifer said, her voice hardly raised above a whisper, "It was just a dream, wasn't it, Robert? Or some sort of illusion. It wasn't real."

"It *was* real," said Robert quietly. "Perhaps even more real than this."

"But it's still Friday morning, isn't it?" Jennifer asked anxiously. "We haven't been gone for days, have we?"

"It's Saturday morning," answered Robert. "People are out looking for us."

"*Saturday* morning?"

Haltingly, Robert told the story of his journey from Smailholm Tower to Locharden, and of the miracle of finding Duncan. Jennifer listened, fighting against believing that it could all really have happened.

"You'll have to believe it's true when you see Duncan," Robert told her. "He even saw Kartan."

They were climbing up through the bracken now, almost hidden by the coarse leaves. A throbbing sound filled the air, and looking back, they saw a helicopter circling the stones like a giant insect. Then it moved off toward the coast.

"It's out looking for us," Robert whispered, but they stayed where they were, concealed by the bracken.

"Do you think Kartan got back to his own people?" Jennifer asked slowly, finally accepting that the experience was far bigger than a dream. "I hope he found his way back."

Then it was her turn to tell Robert how the Bearded One had forced her to go back to Kelso, and that the Barbaric Ones had taken many of the brown people captive.

"It didn't make any difference that we were there," said Robert sadly. "Kartan thought at first that we had come to save them."

"I only made things worse," Jennifer agreed. "You should have seen how awful Savotar looked when he struck the Bearded One. He only did it for me."

"Maybe they have changed us," said Robert quietly.

"I was always scared you wanted to stay there," Jennifer confessed. "And then in the end it was me that got left behind. That was awful—those Barbaric Ones and everything. Just the same, I wish we could be sure that Kartan got back to his own people."

They were almost at the Taylor Farm when the searchers found them and hustled them back to the warmth of the Crandall's kitchen. Mrs. Dean was there and had the fire roaring and kettles boiling for tea and soup and hot chocolate for the weary searchers. Some had been out on the moor all night. Mrs. Crandall clung to Jennifer as if she would never let her out of her sight again.

"Just look at your clothes and hair!" Mrs. Crandall

said, brushing off a large, leathery brown leaf that was clinging to Jennifer's denim jeans.

"Suffering from exposure," Mr. MacPherson pronounced to explain Jennifer's dazed look and contradictory answers.

"It's been strange weather," said an old farmer. "I've never seen a fog hang in like that, over just one part of the moor. Clear all day here in the glen yesterday, and yet the old stone circle was cut off by the fog. That's where they were wandering."

The Guthries were there, and Duncan, too. Duncan kept an eye on Robert but did not speak to him until they were on their way home and far enough ahead of their parents to be out of hearing.

"We'll leave it the way it is, Robert, that you were out on the moor. It would only hurt them if they thought that you had run away too. But I still don't get it. That other kid you were with—where is he now? And the girl—where was she yesterday?"

"I'll tell you some time," said Robert. "But, please, not right now."

Hearing the weariness in his voice, Duncan did not press him.

It was a week before either Mrs. Crandall or the Guthries would hear of Jennifer or Robert going anywhere other than school. Even then Jennifer's mother insisted on going with them, but that was all right. They wanted to visit Robert's grandfather, old Dougal Ballentyne, in Baldry, and it was easier to have Mrs. Crandall take them in the car than time their visit to fit in with the sporadic bus service that linked Locharden and Baldry.

Robert and Jennifer had seen each other at school, of course, and had talked guardedly about their adventure, but they had found that it was rather a relief to immerse themselves in the dull routine of school and not think too much about what they had seen. Yet they both felt a need to share the experience, and Robert was so sure that his grandfather was the right person to tell, that Jennifer finally agreed to go along with him.

The visit was planned for Saturday afternoon. When Mrs. Crandall came to pick up Robert, Duncan was out in the yard working on the tractor.

"I see your brother hasn't gone back to Edinburgh yet," she remarked to Robert as he climbed into the back seat of the car.

"He's not going back," said Robert. "He's taken a job in a garage in Baldry for a bit and is living over there now. That way he can get home on weekends and help out."

"How nice for your parents!"

"For me, too," said Robert with a grin. "It leaves less work for me to do."

"And I heard old MacPherson telling your dad when they were at our house that morning what a great artist you are," said Jennifer. "Really laying it on thick!"

"I heard him, too," said Robert. "It was decent of

him considering the last thing of mine he saw was a picture of him I drew on the blackboard! But it would take more than old MacPherson to change my dad's mind about something."

"It can't hurt," said Jennifer.

In no time at all they reached the row of drab stucco council houses on the outskirts of Baldry where old Mr. Ballentyne lived. Robert was relieved when Mrs. Crandall said she wouldn't come in now because she had shopping she wanted to do in Baldry.

"It will take me about two hours," she said as she drove away.

The children let themselves into the house and found the old man sitting in an armchair with a tartan blanket thrown over his knees, staring at the single glowing bar of a small electric heater.

"It's not like a peat fire," he complained. "There's no smell and no company sitting by this wee metal thing."

"I've brought you something," said Robert, sitting down on the rag rug by his grandfather's feet, just as he used to.

Robert unbuttoned his shirt and drew out the little picture of the stones and the swirling mists that Kartan had painted.

Jennifer gasped. "You kept it," she said, coming over and sitting down beside him. "You brought it back from their time. How could you do that?"

"I carried it buttoned up inside my shirt all the time," said Robert.

177

"It's a bonny picture," said the old man, looking at it casually and then letting it fall into his lap.

"Do you know where it is?" Robert asked anxiously. "Don't you recognize it?"

"I don't see so well now," he said.

Robert switched on a small lamp at the old man's elbow, directing the light onto the picture. The mists in the painting seemed to come alive, swirling around the stones, and the kneeling figures were suddenly sharply in focus.

"It's the old stones," said his grandfather, and new life came into his voice. "The Stones of Arden."

"I wanted you to have it because you always liked that place," said Robert eagerly.

"Aye, these stones have always had a strange hold over me. There's more to them than most people realize. This picture—it puts me in mind of the day your mother, Meg, was lost on the moor. Just a wee bit of a lass, she was, scarce able to toddle. She wandered away from the croft and the mist came down."

While Jennifer and Robert listened in spellbound silence, the old man told them the story of the day when he, too, had been lost in the Circle of Time. On reaching the stone circle, in a frenzy of grief at losing his child, he had fallen to his knees, tearing at the black peat. The mists had parted and he found himself in this other place, a wooded place, and the stones were now close to the sea.

"There I was, on a clifftop, looking down on a

wide bay, where the sea had taken a great bite out of the land. I had never seen that part of the coast before. A boat was being pulled up on the beach by a group of tall brown people, splashing through the shallow water in bare feet.

"I was not alone watching the boat. Quite close to me, almost close enough to touch, stood a tall man with long black hair. He had a gray cloak over his shoulders—I was to remember that later—and around his neck, on a cord, was a small green whistle. It was such an odd thing that I noticed it in particular.

"A little farther along the clifftop were two other people. A bonny girl, tall and brown-skinned like the young man, and she had a gold cross around her neck hanging from a chain. Beside her was a lad, shorter than the other two, with curly hair and lighter skin.

"They did not see me because their eyes were fixed on the boat on the beach. Suddenly the tall man called out, 'Panchros! Alloperla! You have come back at last!' He went scrambling down a steep path to the beach, taking with him a hail of loose stones in his haste. He ran across the sand and threw himself into the open arms of the brown people, who came running up the beach to meet him.

"The other two followed more slowly. The curly-haired lad had some trouble getting down the steep path, and I noticed that he favored one leg a bit when he ran across the sand.

"Their great happiness at finding each other reminded me again of my own loss, and I turned and went back to the stone circle.

"Perhaps I slept. I do not remember now. There was a coldness and a quiet, and when I came to myself again, I found my little Meg. She was lying asleep by a stone, quite unharmed, and she was wrapped in a soft gray cloak just like the one the tall man had been wearing."

"It was Kartan and Lara Avara," Robert whispered.

"I took her home, and have told no one until now the whole story of that strange vision at the Stones of Arden."

"It couldn't have been them," said Jennifer, breaking the silence that had settled on the room.

"It *was* them," Robert insisted. "But older than when we knew them. Alloperla and Panchros and the others must have escaped from the Barbaric Ones and returned to the Far Northlands. Don't you understand? It was *after* we were there."

"But how can you be so sure?"

"The green whistle. A boy gave Kartan a green whistle when we were on the bus to Edinburgh. I'd forgotten about it till now. But don't you see? It was something from our time, so Kartan kept it and wore it. And *you* gave Lara Avara the cross."

"And who was the other young man?" Jennifer asked, a challenging note in her voice. "The curly-haired one who limped?"

Robert remembered the tearing pain he had experienced at the stones. . . . But he would think about that later—it was too incredible, too wonderful . . .

The old man looked questioningly at their excited faces.

"We've been there, too," said Robert. Then he and Jennifer, interrupting each other in their eagerness, told him all they could remember.

They were still talking when Mrs. Crandall came back. She paused in the doorway, looking at the three bright faces—two very young and one lined with age—in the circle of light cast by the small lamp. The place was poorly furnished, without even the comfort of a fireplace, and the walls were bare of pictures; but the two children and the old man seemed to be lost in an enchantment of their own making that brightened the whole drab room.

MARGARET J. ANDERSON is recognized as a storyteller of special gifts. "Anderson's simple, almost stark prose is most expressive," praised *School Library Journal* of SEARCHING FOR SHONA. "She allows us to share her insight with a very special story bound to keep us in its spell," concluded *Language Arts* in praise of IN THE KEEP OF TIME. And *The New York Times Book Review* named TO NOWHERE AND BACK An Outstanding Book of the Year 1975, citing it as "a fascinating, carefully thought-out and credible journey through a time warp."

In addition to her novels, Margaret J. Anderson has written numerous articles and books for children on science and ecology.

She was born and educated in Scotland and graduated from the University of Edinburgh with honors in genetics. She now lives in Corvallis, Oregon with her husband and four children.